Margaret Benkema
Washington   D. C.
Christmas 1976

W9-AQA-770

MEMOIRS

OF

A LONDON DOLL,

Written by Herself.

EDITED BY MRS FAIRSTAR
(*Otherwise Mr Richard Henry Horne*)

WITH AN INTRODUCTION AND NOTES
BY MARGERY FISHER

With four Illustrations,

BY MISS MARGARET GILLIES

And Additional Decorations

BY RICHARD SHIRLEY SMITH

LONDON:
JOSEPH CUNDALL, 12 OLD BOND ST.,
1846
THE MACMILLAN COMPANY, NEW YORK

INTRODUCTION AND NOTES
COPYRIGHT © 1967 BY MARGERY FISHER

ALL RIGHTS RESERVED. NO COPYRIGHTED COMPONENT
PART OF THIS BOOK MAY BE REPRODUCED OR TRANSMITTED IN
ANY FORM OR BY ANY MEANS, ELECTRONIC OR MECHANICAL,
INCLUDING PHOTOCOPYING, RECORDING OR BY ANY
INFORMATION STORAGE AND RETRIEVAL SYSTEM,
WITHOUT PERMISSION IN WRITING FROM
THE PUBLISHER.

LIBRARY OF CONGRESS CATALOG CARD NUMBER: 68-18475

PRINTED IN THE UNITED STATES OF AMERICA

FIRST PRINTING

Contents.

INTRODUCTION

Writing to his friend Elizabeth Barrett in the 1840's, Richard Henry Horne mentioned "a sort of Christmas book for children, called *The London Doll*", which he had written not long before. It was not publicly acknowledged as his, though, until many years later. Horne loved mystification and indulged in pseudonyms even more than his contemporaries did. When he contributed an article on *The True and Froggy Art of Swimming* to *Fraser's Magazine* he called himself Sir Julius Cutwater: a satirical biography of Van Ambergh the lion-tamer purported to be by a New York hardware dealer called Ephraim Watts: elsewhere he might be Lucius O'Trigger or Salim ben Uzair or Pycle, as the occasion demanded. *Memoirs of a London Doll* is "written by herself" and "edited by Mrs Fairstar"—perhaps with special point, for this most charming of Victorian nursery tales uses a name sometimes given to little nursery lapdogs.

In middle life Horne went further in borrowing from an acquaintance the name Hengist, to replace his own more ordinary middle name. Richard Hengist Horne (for so he is more generally known) was a Protean character in more than his names. A life of alternate excitement in action and intense reflection: a considerable body of works, no two of which are really alike: an appearance bizarre and yet inspiring confidence—he stands out even in such an age of unselfconscious individualists.

Richard Horne was born in Edmonton in 1802 and died at Margate in 1884. As a boy, at Cowden Clarke's school at Enfield, he threw a snowball at Keats: Edmund Gosse recalls seeing him, as an old man, bending a poker by striking it on his braced arm. He moved through this long life in a way which could not be ignored. His contemporaries admired him but thought him vain. He seemed one of those people who must always *present* themselves. It was always the unusual niches he filled, the out of the way subjects he wrote about. From comments about him in letters it seems that his friends were sometimes puzzled by his constantly changing literary plans. He reacted quickly and positively to the outside world and was always very assured in putting his impressions into literary forms, always ready to experiment with them. Perhaps too ready—for he passed so rapidly from one kind of writing to another that he never reached the first rank in any of them. There is another side to this. Horne had to earn his living, and some of his writing (whether in criticism, journalism, drama or poetry) was done, not wholly but initially, because it would bring him money quickly.

He did not at first intend to be a writer. As the son of an army man he was sent from school to Sandhurst when he was sixteen. He did not complete the four-year course, and after a period probably spent in London he joined the Mexican Navy, serving as a midshipman on the *Libertad* under an English captain. After some time on the fringes of naval warfare, he made his way through North America and Canada, returning to England in about 1828. These years of travel, whatever they had given him in experience, hardly counted as a useful apprenticeship. He had learned to play the guitar and his repertoire of Spanish songs became familiar at social gatherings to the end of his life, but to make a living he must look elsewhere. He had been writing intermittently for some years, and it must have been easy for him to exchange adventure in action for adventurousness in print.

Something of his Mexican days was carried over—the guitar and the songs, but also the almost gaucho appearance due to his cape and his particular choice of face-covering. Macready's comment on his "horrid moustaches" and Harriet Martineau's on his "somewhat coxcombical curling whiskers" are filled out by Elizabeth Barrett's more detailed description of a miniature of him, in a letter to Miss Mitford:

> "Imagine a high-browed and broad-browed head, absolutely bald, appearing to the fancy as if all the glistening auburn ringlets belonging to it, had fallen down to the base of the head and expended themselves in whiskers and moustachios! The features are very handsome—the nose delicate and aquiline, the eyes a clear blue, serene and elevated—the mouth strikingly expressive of resolution— the complexion quite colorless, almost to ghastliness— with a Rembrandt light full on it . . . Somebody cried out 'It's like an assassin',—and somebody else 'It's like a saint,' A very fine head certainly!—with a fifth Act in the very look of it! But I deprecate the moustache, and half believe and hope that it has been cut away since the picture was painted." (December 6, 1842. Quoted in *Elizabeth Barrett to Miss Mitford* ed. Betty Miller, 1954, p. 151.)

Miss Barrett's hope was not fulfilled. Turner met Horne when he was an old man and was disillusioned "to see in the famous poet, a little thick-set man with a white wrinkled face, a bald head, with straggling locks of curly hair hanging over his coat collar behind, and a carefully curled long drooping moustache in front".

The literary world of the 1830's might have been made for just such a versatile man as Horne. Family magazines and literary journals were multifarious, and packed with tiny print in double columns. They had two watchwords—variety and topicality. There were favourite subjects (amelioration of the life of the poor, the new colonies in Australia and New Zealand), but a place for articles on almost anything. Horne's flexible prose was formed in pieces for the *Monthly Repository* (which he edited between June 1836 and July 1837), in the *Monthly Chronicle* under Leigh Hunt, in the *Monthly Magazine*, the *New Quarterly*, the *Church of England Quarterly*, *Fraser's*, *Howitt's Journal*, and for Dickens in the *Daily News* and *Household Words*. The ease with which he chooses a style and sustains it in *Memoirs of a London Doll* is the ease of a thoroughly professional writer.

Horne wanted to be a great deal more than a journalist. But ephemeral pieces might well suit present day taste better than the works he set most store by. Apart from his articles, some of his longer published works are occasional pieces. They show his knack of choosing odd, unexpected literary forms which turn out to be perfectly appropriate for what he wanted to say. The title of one of his early books is provocative—*Exposition of the False Medium and Barriers Excluding Men of Genius from the Public*. His arguments could as well have been presented quite straight in a magazine article. Instead, Horne wrote a whole book so bursting with facts and ideas that at first reading it seems incoherent. But he has chosen the right form for attacking the stupidity and prejudice of reviewers and theatre managers and for the deeper plea that great creative talent must be free to break with orthodox forms and platforms. He works out his ideas with some historical progression (incidentally, the book is a valuable index to the taste of his time) and there are touches of the freakish hilarity that is unlike the humour of any other writer. This hilarity is still more noticeable in *Spirit of Peers and People*, which he called a National Tragi-Comedy. This dramatic burlesque crusades for the man in the street who has no say in a government dominated by crown, nobility and church. Like so much of Horne's work it is far ahead of its time, and there is plenty to interest readers today besides the (to us) astonishingly disrespectful portrait of William IV and his court.

Horne's serious reputation rested on poetic drama. He was foremost among the writers who tried to bring back the glories of the English stage, and his tragedies—*The Death of Marlowe, Gregory VII* and *Judas Iscariot*—are (the first especially) notable in the Jacobean manner. A reputation of a rather different kind came with the publication of *A New Spirit of the Age* in 1844. In this collection of critical essays on his contemporaries he was helped (anonymously) by Elizabeth Barrett, who had already worked with him by correspondence on modernisations of Chaucer; but Horne bore the attacks from those who were dissatisfied with his judgment, and the book was in many quarters severely mauled. The essays (entirely by Horne) on Browning and Dickens especially give a valuable idea of their standing at this particular date.

At his death, though, Horne was probably best known for a work that gave him yet another name—"Orion Horne". *Orion*, an epic poem in the same *genre* as *Hyperion*, was published in 1843 by the Oxford Street bookseller, Miller. He was instructed that the poem was not to be sold to anyone who pronounced its title with a short "i" and that nobody could have more than one copy. *Orion* was priced at a farthing —and no change was to be given. These conditions were variously interpreted. Some (like Elizabeth Barrett) thought they reflected Horne's poor opinion of the reading public, others that it was all done for advertisement. Horne himself said years later that he was trying to make a price at which unlikely people could read the poem. At all events, the whole affair was typical of him.

It was this man, with his lofty view of man's potentiality, his strong individual imagery and bold ideas, this man regarded as a writer of weight and power, who sat down to write the memoirs of a doll, in a style exquisitely suitable, without condescension or bathos, and in a spirit of evident enjoyment. Why?

In these early years of Victoria's reign it would be true to say that, in the literary world, everybody knew everybody. The interlinked circles of Horne's acquaintance show this very well. Among scientists, Dr Southwood Smith stood out, the reformer of London's sanitation; among radicals, the Unitarian, W. J. Fox; in theatrical circles, Macready and Serjeant Talfourd. Horne discussed his poetry with Browning (and with Elizabeth Barrett on paper, for she had no visitors). He visited Miss Mitford in Berkshire (though she disapproved of his manners). He belonged to a group of disappointed authors and philosophers calling themselves the Syncretics, and to a more convivial group of men and women, brought together by Douglas Jerrold under the formidable title of The Whittington Club and Metropolitan Athenaeum. He acted in some of the amateur theatricals which amused Dickens, Mark Lemon and others of the *Punch* group. His acquaintance with writers was extended when he worked on the staff of the *Daily News* and *Household Words*.

He belonged by right of friendship and kindred ideas to a more domestic circle as well. During the 1840's two houses saw a considerable output of good writing for children. In Clapton, first at The Grange and then at The Elms, the Quaker Mary Howitt was producing tales for children and young people, stories mainly of country scenes and people, full of sweetness and good sense. At this time, too, she and her husband, William, were involved with the *People's Journal*, a magazine for the pleasure and education of the uneducated, which William Howitt took over from its proprietor wholly in 1847 after financial disputes. The last of Horne's stories for children, *King Penguin*, was serialised in *Howitt's Journal of Literature and Popular Progress* in 1848.

In the Howitt household Horne met and talked with Eliza Cook (herself editor of a magazine for "the lower classes") and with Caroline Hill, Southwood Smith's daughter, who held progressive views on education. In this liberal middle-class household Horne found, or confirmed, his ideas about children and the kind of books they should read. He was at this time a bachelor and his marriage in 1847 to Catherine Foggo did not really change his habit of life very much. They had no children, and he seems to have found family life only through his friends. The youngest Howitt children, Charlton and Margaret, were nine and seven when the *London Doll* was published, and their playmate, Octavia Hill, Caroline's daughter, was ten. There was plenty of material to build theories on, but plenty of fun as well. Letters surviving from Mary Howitt to Eliza Meteyard (another author of stories for the young) refer to a children's party with a magic lantern to which she had invited Horne, among others, "to give dignity to the party"—but Horne also sent along beforehand his guitar and a bag of "properties". Parts of his doll story suggest a friendly knowledge of actual children (for instance, the description of Ellen Plummy taking her medicine, and of a visit to the Zoo); and there surely must be private allusions and jokes in the story.

One of Mary Howitt's letters invites Miss Meteyard to spend a day and a night at Clapton "as our friend Mary Gillies will be here and I want you to know and love her." The two Miss Gillies lived at this time in Highgate and a little later in Hampstead. Margaret Gillies was well-known as a water-colourist and also as an illustrator of children's books. The earliest illustrations for the *London Doll* were her work, and though to modern eyes her drawings seem a little stodgy, they show that she knew the story well and liked it. Her sister, Mary, worked in collaboration with Horne during the 1840's, first on his *History of Napoleon* (1841) and then along different lines.

Mary Gillies herself may have been the initiator of the series of stories for young children which she and Horne wrote for the publisher, Joseph Cundall, and which he produced in delectable little volumes, often for the Christmas market. One reviewer said:

> "The mere sight of the little books . . . is as good as a nosegay. Their actual covers are as brilliant as a bed of tulips, and blaze with emerald, and orange, and cobalt, and gold, and crimson . . . "
> (*Fraser's Magazine for Town and Country*, vol 33 (Jan-June 1846, p. 497)

These publications were known as the "Myrtle" books and the "author" (at this time certainly a composite one) was "Mrs Harriet Myrtle." A very fair description of the Myrtle books may be found in the *London Doll*. Little Emmy at the pastrycook's read aloud to her sister, and the doll eagerly listened to "pretty stories of little boys and girls, and affectionate mammas and aunts, and kind old nurses, and birds in the fields and woods, and flowers in the gardens and hedges". Horne takes writer's licence to advertise his wares by name. After mentioning Mary Howitt's *Birds and Flowers* and Mrs Marcet's stories of Willie, he goes on to speak of "the delightful little books of Mrs Harriet Myrtle,—in which I did *so* like to hear about old Mr Dove, the village carpenter, and little Mary, and the account of May Day, and the Day in the Woods,—and besides other books, there was oh! *such* a story-book called 'The Good-natured Bear'!" The last-named story was Horne's own and there is some evidence that the May Day story was also his. It has an abundance of concrete detail of a kind less evident in some other stories in the series. Another story known to be Horne's, *The Man of Snow*, was too long for the publisher's scheme and he asked Horne to shorten it. But though Horne tried to comply, he found the details he had used essential to the story. "Children do like and delight in circumstantial details," he wrote to Cundall; "they have not knowledge enough, and experience, to fill up the blanks of concise writing. In three pages and a half, or four pages, there is scarcely time to get up any interest—and no sooner is it got up than it ends. This will never do".* In another Myrtle story, *The New Kite*, he begs indulgence for something quite new in children's books "of the amusing kind"—diagrams: but the publisher must "be sure to direct that all the diagrams are made *correct according to the measurements stated*—for we may be certain that the children will set to work to measure them, to see if they are right." His painstaking attitude to detail is conspicuous in the *London Doll*. He was not able to see the Lord Mayor's Show of 1845, which he used in the story, and after he had sent Cundall the manuscript he followed it with a revision which he insisted was necessary. "I had my doubts and sent two friends with Notebooks to see the last Show. The revision is from their notes. I wish to *see* the revise, if you please." The neat realism in the story helps to stiffen it and to balance its sweet simplicity.

* The letters from Horne to Cundall quoted here and in the following pages are now in the Henry Huntington Library in California.

Horne and Mary Gillies tried to keep their styles distinct so that the little books would be pleasantly varied, but their agreement was complete as to the note of family affection and pleasure which informs them. Certain trends may be traced in children's literature during the first half of the nineteenth century, with the usual exceptions to the rule. In the '40's, as in the 1800's, it was expected that children would *profit* from their reading. But by the '40's instruction was easier, the prevailing manner more relaxed, the moral less intrusive, the aim to touch the imagination more than the reason. An anonymous reviewer makes the point in 1846:

"What is it that constitutes a good child's book? Is it to put difficult knowledge in as unattractive a form as possible; to make fathers and mothers cold and dry preceptors; is it to strew as many thorns and thistles as possible along the newly macadamised road to knowledge? No, not according to our notions! We think that the true spirit of a child's book ought to be love and cheerfulness, leaving the scholastic knowledge to come in the professedly school-books."
(*The People's Journal*, vol. I. 1846, p. 322)

He ends with a warm appreciation of the books he is reviewing—no less than the first Myrtle story-books, *The Good-Natured Bear* and the *London Doll*.

Horne claimed that he and Mary Gillies were trying to do something new in these little books. Certainly the stories confirm, and so do letters to and from Horne and his friends, that there was in the Howitt and Gillies households a spirit of enjoyment and of free, open affection for children which must have had its effect. The Howitt family was a commonalty, much like the family in which Mrs Ewing's talents

grew. Discipline in such homes was not restrictive: it was
more a matter of organising life intelligently to give freedom
for proper growth. In many articles on education at this time
the image of plants recurs—plants which must be staked and
pruned but which need, above all, sun and moisture for their
well-being.

Horne, who so often demanded "pure air and abundant
water" for London's poor, knew that children needed
intellectual equivalents of these as well. Often obtrusive
and tactless with adults, he had also a gentleness which is
evident in the stories he wrote for children.

This side of Horne is epitomised in the title of his book,
The Good-Natured Bear, which he and others seemed to use
almost as a nickname. It was certainly his favourite among
his stories for children and he was teased for comparing it
with Robinson Crusoe and Gulliver. "I only said it was of
the same *family*", he protested to Cundall, "and surely . . .
one may claim to be a 'poor relation' without offence."

He wrote the story in 1844 when he was in Germany, much
of the time staying at Bonn. From here he sent stories for the
Myrtle books which Cundall and Mary Gillies were assemb-
ling in London. "I had always intended to write a Christmas
Story for you", he wrote to Cundall on 19 December, "but
no satisfactory idea occurred to me till a few days ago. Since
which I have worked away, and done nothing else." Obviously
pleased with the story, he suggested a more substantial
payment than he had received for the earlier stories, for the
Bear was "a regular design, and of far more skill and
structure". The story has a German domestic setting, vividly
realising what Horne had seen himself during his long visit.
A large and happy family is entertained at Christmas time
by a bear who, in a voice of ursine timbre and grave humour,
tells the story of his life. We discover at the very end that the

Bear is Uncle Abraham, whose disguise has been assumed to entertain the children and also to attract the attention of the pretty nursery governess. Browning hit off the character of the little book exactly when he called it "furry, warm and genial". Horne went to a great deal of trouble to get it exactly right. He revised some parts "with a view to greater simplicity—except in those passages where a little heightening is intended to produce an effect of wonder and interest in the child by its very obscurity and strangeness." He is particular about the illustrations. They must be amusing, but he hopes the artist has given Uncle Abraham "a pleasant countenance —agreeable and humorous—not too old—and on no account ugly"—for this would disappoint the children when the dénouement was reached. He writes anxiously about the type, the reviewing and advertising of the book, and hopes that Prince Albert (who evidently received a presentation copy) was amused "at certain references to Bonn, where he was a student". In short, the *Bear* was Horne's book; and even though at first he wished to remain anonymous, he could not resist dropping hints, and even writing a rather heavily whimsical pair of letters for *Howitt's Journal*, one from a supposed reader inviting the Bear to come and growl at her house, the other a friendly reply.

The *Good-Natured Bear* was not published till 1846 (Horne was displeased that Cundall missed the Christmas market of 1845) and by this time the *London Doll* was ready too. A letter to Cundall dated October 1845 emphasised how different this story is. Horne wrote:

"I cannot (wisely) oppose your better judgment in the matter of illustrations for the 'Doll'—particularly as I have not yet seen any of Mr Taylor's drawings for the 'Bear'. I only know that if he does the 'Doll' (having done the

'Bear' well) he will be most likely to choose points of *humour*, and to execute them in a way that Miss M. Gillies could not; but that if she did the illustrations, she would select those points interesting to children for their pretty and pleasing sweetness. Each artist would do what individual nature and talent dictated. It is for you to decide which would best answer the purpose, and subject."

Once again Horne was utterly, professionally absorbed in what he was writing. In January of the next year he wrote to explain to his publisher that the "Editress" of the doll story was to be "Mrs Fairstar",

"because if this be successful, [it] would justify a series (such as Memoirs of a *Country* Doll—Memoirs of a *French* Doll—Memoirs of a *Dutch* Doll (or German &c.) then the whole series might so well be called as No. 1 or No. 2 &c. of 'Mrs Fairstar's Dolls'. Don't you see?"

Horne must have got some way in the planning of a sequel about a country doll, for there are the two little creatures together in the foreground of the frontispiece to the first edition of the *London Doll*. (This is the first of the four drawings by Margaret Gillies reproduced in the endpapers of the present edition.) But so far as I know no sequel was ever published, possibly because children's stories were not sufficiently well paid for a man living by his pen. We do know that in 1847 Horne was subsidised by Douglas Jerrold to write a novel, *The Dreamer and the Worker*, which was serialised in *Jerrold's Shilling Magazine*. Apart from the *London Doll*, 1846 saw the publication of a pantomime, *The Ill-Used Giant, Being a new and true version of "Jack and the Beanstalk"*. This is a rackety piece of very moderate value. The Myrtle books continued but it is not known how far Horne was concerned with them. The last story for children that is certainly his is *King Penguin* (1848), an odd, rather stiff little fantasy about a Jack Tar shipwrecked on an island whose avian inhabitants are ruled by a highly educated and arrogant King. The story is entertaining but it has (as, indeed, the *Good-Natured Bear* has) a great deal of rambling adult comment in it. The *London Doll* shows best of all the relaxed and delicate artistry of these years when Horne stood level with children and shared their pleasures of imagination.

In the neatly planned chronicle of the *London Doll* he has skilfully combined three points of view—those of the adult, the children, and the doll. The whole conception of the story is adult. The mock-autobiography (of a mouse, a shilling, an old chair and so on) was accepted in the last century as a way of presenting a panorama of social life in town or country, and Horne's story can be read in this way. But it is first and foremost a *story*, depending on Maria Poppet the doll and on the various little girls who successively make a home for her. Their portraits are drawn affectionately and realistically by Horne, and the doll concurs in his love for them: her tart and caustic remarks (in that voice so often heard in doll stories) are reserved for the vagaries of adult life. To Horne the children are truly the "little mammas" the doll calls them. Ellen Plummy at the pastrycook's and the clerk's daughter, Mary Hope, both make clothes for her: Lady Flora lives in Hanover Square and has not been accustomed to sew, but she explains the sights of the West End to her. As for Italian Brigitta, when she and her brother climbed into a derelict house in Cheapside to see the procession, "the first thing she did was to station me between two broken bricks at the side of the window, so that I could look down from this height upon the whole of the Lord Mayor's Show as it passed in the street beneath". Each child looks after the doll in the way her particular capabilities suggest—and her particular social sphere. In so short a story, with so many children to introduce, Horne draws his characters with remarkable skill. He has obviously taken trouble to get the details of dress and behaviour exactly right, but he has realised the little girls as individuals as well. We see very little of any one of them but we know perfectly what each one is like.

For a writer as original and intelligent as Horne, the doll provides a perfect opportunity for wit. Maria is neither child nor adult, but, consistently, doll. A little arrogantly, very observantly, she surveys the world, dividing the folk in it into ordinary humans, little mammas, and dolls—this last group including anyone who is unusually rigged out, as it were in fancy dress. Thus, the Lord Mayor and his supporters seem to her to be dolls (wooden like herself) in the same way as the statues of Achilles and the Duke of York and the figures of Gog and Magog at the Guildhall.

Of course, Horne was writing for the children of his acquaintance and for all those who were educated to read intelligently. But his story grew also out of his concern for children less fortunate than those who had his books as presents—children who, if they could read at all, might know Jack the Giant Killer or "a bit of Robinson Crusoe", but often little more. In 1841 (a few years before the *London Doll*) Horne had been appointed to act as one of twenty Assistant Commissioners in a government investigation of child labour in mines and factories. One of the four Commissioners was his friend Dr Southwood Smith. General instructions were given to examine the children "by themselves, and not in the presence of their parents or employers; and to take every precaution . . . to diminish the chances of inaccuracy of statement, from timidity, or from the confusion

to which Children are subject when spoken to by a stranger".
Horne's district was in and around Wolverhampton, his
brief with those working in metal-goods factories, producing
nails, screws, steel pins and so on. His reports are full of
facts distressing to read. He wrote with telling restraint
but feeling shows more strongly at times. He described, for
instance, the "little iron bar" which was put in front of a
nail machine, a pitifully minimal safety device:

" . . . to prevent a child who happens to be forgetful from
putting its fingers into the cutting aperture. That the
accidents which are so continually occurring . . . are
attributable to 'carelessness' is, no doubt, for the most
part very true; but let us look at the offence compara-
tively. A Child of the upper or middle classes is practising
on the piano-forte: this Child does not go over the finger-
ing of the same unvarying passage from hour to hour,
from day to day, from year to year; but has an interesting
variety in its practice. Yet the most apt scholar and most
assiduous practiser will now and then miss its distances,
and be a little out of its time. It is precisely for this offence
that one of these poor Children, working in support of
itself, and perhaps of its infirm mother, loses a finger or
has its hand smashed; and for the carelessness of one
second of time is mutilated during the remainder of its
life."
(*State Papers* vol. 13, *Children's Employment* [*Trades and
Manufactures*] 1843, p. 415)

In another moving passage (p. 495) Horne described the
children's prayers. When they told him they said "Our
Father" at night he had assumed they meant the whole
prayer but discovered they knew only the first two words.

When the Commission's report was published in 1843, Elizabeth Barrett read it and was so much affected by this passage in Horne's evidence that she wrote, at white heat of emotion, the poem *The Cry of the Children*, which appeared in *Blackwood's* soon afterwards.

To write benevolently of "the poor" was by no means unusual in the 1840's; it is the time, after all, of *David Copperfield* and *The Old Curiosity Shop*, of Mrs Trollope's *Michael Armstrong the Factory Boy*. It is not surprising that when Horne was planning his doll's varied life he should include some children in humble circumstances. But his principles about children's reading would certainly prevent him from introducing into his story anything sordid or distressing. If sadness and pathos were to be there as well as sweetness and pleasure, they must be presented in due proportion. He did not choose to put his poor children into any of the trades he had investigated himself, but for one of them, Ellen Plummy, he chose the milliner's trade (a far wider term then than now), which had come under the same Commission. He would know from the official report that five-year-old children worked as long as seventeen hours in a day, that they were often brutally treated, that they were given backless chairs to sit on so that they would not relax and slow down their work, that they had scanty food to eat and scant time to eat it. Little Ellen goes to work for her Aunt Sharpshins when she is nine and she has a hard time of it, with little sleep or rest and no time for play. But all this is background to the happy picture of two little girls (a bad cold has lent them for once a little free time) sewing for Maria Poppet a fine dress of lemon-coloured merino with a violet sash, under a tent made of bedclothes to keep them warm (and Aunt Sharpshins had at least given Ellen the scraps of material). Horne is quite definite about the poverty of Marco and Brigitta, about the over-crowding in the garret of the doll-making Sprats and the frugal diet of the little girl who plays Columbine in the pantomime; but he makes these things tolerable by the affection and grace implicit in their lives. The laughter between Brigitta and her brother, the happy relationship little Columbine enjoys with the grandmother who plays the dragon, were clearly meant to reassure the young reader.

Memoirs of a London Doll is in more than one sense "a sort of Christmas book for children". It belongs with the newly translated stories of Hans Andersen and with the German-derived Christmas customs, with Dickens's Christmas tales and with those seasonal publications in miniature which one reviewer thought "far better and more appropriate gifts for children than toys or sweetmeats, and much more likely to prove of wholesome and lasting influence". Wholesome as Horne's story is, it is no tract, but a story to give pleasure—and, incidentally, to give a picture of the London year. It runs from a Christmas to a Christmas, starting with Twelfth Night festivities and ending with a pantomime, and taking us on a miniscule tour of the city in the 1840's— Holborn, Regent's Park, Bloomsbury, Hyde Park, Finsbury, Cheapside—in a series of vignettes drawn with gusto as well as knowledge. Small wonder that Caroline Hewins,* who read the story in her American nursery not so many years after its first publication, should feel that all "aided in making London as real to me as Boston."

Like his fellow-journalist Henry Mayhew, Horne tramped this great, growing mass of overcrowding and dirt, with its monstrous contrasts of poverty and riches, finding stories in dust-heaps and railway-stations, fire brigades and parks, docks and cattle-yards, the river and the Zoo. Mayhew's

---

* *A Mid-Century Child and her Books.* Macmillan 1926, p. 119.

articles, published fortnightly in the *Morning Post*, described various slum quarters of London, mainly in faithfully reported conversations with the inhabitants. The articles were later published, in three volumes under the title *London Labour and the London Poor*. Mayhew was in the best sense a reforming journalist. In the London he knew, it was possible for the well-to-do to ignore almost totally the disgraceful social inequalities of the city. Mayhew was determined that they *should* know how the poor lived and how lack of education debarred them from living in any other way. His work was in print only five years after Horne's doll story which, more generally and more gently, makes the same points.

For his times, though, Horne was blessedly lacking in the preachifying tendency. The memoir form, the first-person narrative, certainly helps him, but without his endearing interpretation of Maria Poppet she could so easily have become a vehicle for improvement, as most dolls in stories did at this time. Mrs Trimmer, reviewing Dorothy Kilner's *Dolls' Spelling Books* (1803) in an earlier generation, expresses a view which in Horne's day was still colouring doll stories. She writes:

> "In this pleasing volume we find a little girl acting in the character of a mamma towards her family of Dolls, upon the system of '*make-believe*', and all little mammas of the same description will find much to amuse, and many things to improve them in the lectures which this young lady gives to her wooden and wax children."
> (*The Guardian of Education*, Vol. 2. Jan–August 1803, p. 424)

Twenty years later the anonymous author of *The New Doll, or, Grandmamma's Gift* made it clear that five-year-old Ellen

was given the doll because she was a "wild" child who must
be led to the nursery virtues:

> "By degrees, the doll was made subservient to all the
> purposes of education . . . The love of personal finery was
> banished, for any reward of good behaviour, if given in
> clothes, was confined to a new bonnet or frock for the
> doll; and gluttony, which is generally speaking the great
> sin of childhood, could be effectively decried by the doll's
> example."
> (Anon: *The New Doll, or, Grandmamma's Gift*. London:
> R. Ackerman 1826, p. 21)

Move on nearly thirty years, to the time when Horne's story
was published, and you find the same attitude in *The Doll
and her friends*, or, *Memoirs of the Lady Seraphina* (1852).
This is a charming little book (it was at one time attributed
to Horne) but its chief point is to contrast naughty, provok-
ing Geoffrey with the patient invalid Willy and to trace
the stages of Geoffrey's reformation, which the author neatly
relates to his treatment of the doll. Though Seraphina tells
her own story (to a Pen, in her old age), the author over-
shadows her personality with purpose. As she says in her
preface:

> "My principal intention was to amuse children by a story
> founded on one of their favourite diversions, and to
> inculcate a few such minor morals as my little plot might
> be strong enough to carry; chiefly the domestic happiness
> produced by kind tempers and consideration for others."
> ([Julia Charlotte Maitland]. *The Doll and her Friends*.
> London: Grant and Griffith 1852)

Not as strict as Mrs Trimmer's view, but still there is nothing here to touch the briskly independent, gay and adaptable character of Horne's Maria Poppet, who has something of his own nature in her, just as the Bear has and the Jack Tar of *King Penguin*.

Such reviews as exist of Horne's children's stories accept these as agreeable entertainment, especially to be valued for their essential kindliness. Horne himself believed that children should not be given horrific or sensational books and in an article in *Household Words* (*A Witch in the Nursery*. Sept. 1851, no. 78, pp. 601–609) he condemned the sadistic, amoral aspect of nursery rhymes and fairy tales. In this he was in tune with educational theories current in his day, theories which colour any reviews longer than mere notices. Indeed, children's books, when they were reviewed at all, were most often used as pegs to hang a theory on: there is little real literary criticism of them. For this reason it is hard to find out what Horne's contemporaries really thought about his books for children. The period when he was writing them was a short one and he would have been thought of, justifiably, as an adult writer who for a time had turned to a different sphere. Because education was so important, this was a matter for congratulation. A reviewer in the *People's Journal* grouped together two or three Myrtle books, *The Good-Natured Bear* and the *London Doll*, and wrote in general terms on the common fallacy "that anybody, who can write nothing else, can write a children's book". The reviewer ends thus:

"There is a great deal of genius and knowledge, both of life and books, in these little volumes, which prove that the authors, be they whom they may, are no ordinary people. We have heard of the pen of a well-known and fine poet being in one, at least, of them. We believe it to

be quite possible; and in conclusion say—Dear Mrs
Harriet Myrtle, and deeply-experienced and most good-
natured of Bears, give us many more such books as these;
and excellent Mr Cundall, do all in your power to spread
them far and wide."
(*The People's Journal*, Vol. 1, 1846, p. 322. Possibly by
Mary Howitt)

As the good-natured bear of the nursery Horne was evidently
widely known and loved: his other works failed to make the
impression he desired on his contemporaries. Hurt as much
by lack of interest as by adverse comment, in 1852 he left
England with William Howitt and two of his sons, bound for
Australia and the gold-diggings. Here for the next eighteen
years Horne once more led a life of active adventure—not
with pick and shovel after all, but first commanding Mel-
bourne's Private Gold Escort, later as an assistant Gold
Commissioner, as a barrister's clerk, a prospective Member
of Parliament, an administrator for a government water
scheme, a lecturer, and finally as Mining Registrar and
Surveyor of the Blue Mountain goldfield. These years in
Australia have been carefully and fully described by Cyril
Pearl in *Always Morning* (1960), the only biography of
Horne. He shows the poet growing older, frailer, more
lonely, but always adaptable and always optimistic.

In 1870 Horne returned to England. He expected to pick
things up where he had left them. He found Dickens's
friendship distinctly cooled, England (and London) much
changed, and the whole business of making a living to start
again. The novelist Camilla Toulmin, prominent in early
Victorian literary circles, remembered Horne at the time
when he was renowned as the author of *Orion* and a member
of that exclusive Syncretics Club which she and her friends

were pleased to call the Mutual Admiration Society. When the novelist, as Mrs Newton Crosland, wrote her *Landmarks of a Literary Life 1820–1892*, she recalled how shocked she was to see the alteration in Horne on his return:

> ". . . five and thirty years had of course worked great changes, for he was now quite the old man; his gait was shuffling, and though his eyes still twinkled, they had lost something of their fire."
> (pp. 280–81)

Horne needed all his courage and optimism now. Nobody had paid much attention to his lyrical drama *Prometheus*, which was written in the Australian bush. Nobody wanted the new editions which he prepared of some of his early works, and for some years his application for a pension was refused. He had outlived the time that best suited him. Even then, he seems always to have been one of those writers who are too original for their own good. He was never a comfortable writer (for adults, at least) nor can he easily be contained in a definition.

As for his reputation at the present time, it is safe to say that it hardly exists. From a practical point of view he is not an easy writer to study. His works are almost all out of print, though Eric Partridge's fine edition of *Orion*, published in 1928, must have revived interest in him. Horne is essentially a peripheral figure, mentioned in almost every memoir or collection of letters in his lifetime but rarely discussed at any length. His manuscripts and private papers were dispersed early in the present century. Many of them are now in North American libraries, and the Mitchell Library in Sydney has twenty boxes and more of unsorted Horniana to tantalise scholars on this side of the world. Besides this, a good deal of his work—*Orion*, for example, and the epic *Prometheus*, and his blank verse tragedies—could be read now only as interesting examples from literary history.

His prose is another matter. I would, for instance, like to see in print *The Poor Artist: or, Seven Eyesights and one Object*, a remarkable parable published in 1850 and years ahead of its time in hints of evolution and of impressionism in art; as a study of creative man it deserves to be better known. I would like to see his two prose pieces on Australia bound in with William Howitt's *Land, Labour and Gold*, for these are among the most intelligent and readable products of the early days in the colony. I would like to see a selection of Horne's articles, those which best show that combination of practical fact and highly individual imagination which is so particularly his.

It is this combination, above all, which will endear the *London Doll* to children. But it is not enough in itself to make Horne outstanding as a writer for children—and outstanding he certainly is, just because writing for children was not a limitation for him. When he wrote the *London Doll* he did not feel it necessary to assume a special attitude to life, however carefully he might choose a style and story to suit young readers. All through his doll story the point of view is shifting —from doll to child, from a child to a parent, then back to the doll; but behind it all there is a shrewd, man-of-the-world, clear-eyed, almost sardonic toughness which makes the *London Doll* like nothing else written for children in his day— perhaps like nothing else till Mrs Ewing came along. In his way Horne was a genius, and this book, with its fine balance of intellect and imagination, should go far to prove it.

MARGERY FISHER
ASHTON 1966

ACKNOWLEDGMENTS

I would like to thank the Manuscript Department of the Henry Huntington Library, California, for permission to quote from the Horne-Cundall letters, and the Bodleian Library for allowing the reproduction of the Gillies illustrations.

M.F.

The Memoirs of a London Doll

CHAPTER I.

MY MAKING AND BIRTH.

In a large dusky room at the top of a dusky house in one of the dusky streets of High Holborn, there lived a poor Doll-maker, whose name was Sprat. He was an extremely small man for his age, and not altogether unlike a sprat in the face. He was always dressed in a sort of tight pinafore and trousers, all in one, that fitted close to his body; and this dress was nearly covered with dabs of paint, especially white paint, of which he used most in his work. His family consisted of his wife, and three children—two boys and a girl.

This poor family had but one room, which was at the top of the house. It had no ceiling, but only beams and tiles. It was the workshop by day and the bed-room at night. In the morning, as the children lay in bed, looking up, they could see the light through the chinks in the tiles; and when they went to bed in the evening they could often feel the wind come down, and breathe its cool breath under their nightcaps. Along the wall on one side of the room, farthest from the windows, the beds were laid upon the floor; the largest was for the poor sprat-faced Doll-maker and his wife,—the next largest was for the two boys,—and the smallest, up in the corner, was for the little girl. There were two windows opposite; and a wooden bench, like a long kitchen dresser, extended from one side of the room to the other, close to these windows. Here all the work was done.

This bench was covered with all manner of things;—such as little wooden legs and arms, and wooden heads without hair, and small bodies, and half legs and half arms, which had not yet been fitted together in the joints, and paint pots and painting brushes, and bits of paper and rags of all

colours; and there were tools for cutting and pol-
ishing, and very small hammers, and several old
pill-boxes full of little wooden pegs, and corners of
scouring paper, and small wooden boxes and trays
full of little glass eyes, and glue pots and bits of
wax and bits of leather, and a small red pipkin for
melting wax, and another for melting Indian rubber,
and a broken tea cup for varnish, and several tiny
round bladders, and tiny tin boxes, all full of things
very precious to Mr Sprat in his business.

All the family worked at Doll-making, and were
very industrious. Mr Sprat was of course the great
manager and doer of most things, and always the
finisher, but Mrs Sprat was also clever in her department, which was entirely that of the *eyes*. She either
painted the eyes, or else, for the superior class of
dolls, fitted in the glass ones. She, moreover,
always painted the eye-brows, and was so used to
it, that she could make exactly the same sort of
arch when it was late in the evening and nearly
dark, before candles were lighted. The eldest boy
painted hair; or fitted and glued hair on to the heads
of the best dolls. The second boy fitted half legs
and arms together, by pegs at the joints. The little
girl did nothing but paint rosy cheeks and lips, which
she always did very nicely, though sometimes she

made them rather too red, and looking as if very hot, or blushing extremely.

Now Mr Sprat was very ingenious and clever in his business as a Doll-maker. He was able to make dolls of various kinds, even of wax, or of a sort of composition; and sometimes he did make a few of such materials; but his usual business was to make jointed dolls—dolls who could move their legs and arms in many positions—and these were of course made of wood. Of this latter material I was manufactured.

The first thing I recollect of myself was a kind of a pegging, and pushing, and scraping, and twisting, and tapping down at both sides of me, above and below. These latter operations were the fitting on of my legs and arms. Then, I passed into the hands of the most gentle of all the Sprat family, and felt something delightfully warm laid upon my cheeks and mouth. It was the little girl who was painting me a pair of rosy cheeks and lips; and her face, as she bent over me, was the first object of life that my eyes distinctly saw. The face was a smiling one, and as I looked up at it I tried to smile too, but I felt some hard material over the outside of my face, which my smile did not seem to be able to get through, so I do not think the little girl perceived it.

But the last thing done to me was by Mr Sprat himself, whose funny white face and round eyes I could now see. He turned me about and about in his hands, examining and trying my legs and arms, which he moved backwards and forwards, and up and down, to my great terror, and fixed my limbs in various attitudes. I was so frightened! I thought he would break something off me. However, nothing happened, and when he was satisfied that I was a complete doll in all parts, he hung me up on a line that ran along the room over head, extending from one wall to the other, and near to the two beams that also extended from wall to wall. I hung upon the line to dry, in company with many other dolls, both boys and girls, but mostly girls. The tops of the beams were also covered with dolls, all of whom, like those on the lines, were waiting there till their paint or varnish had properly dried and hardened. I passed the time in observing what was going on in the room under my line, and also the contents of the room, not forgetting my numerous little companions, who were all smiling and staring, or sleeping, round about me.

Mr Sprat was a Doll-maker only; he never made doll's clothes. He said *that* was not work for an artist like him. So in about a week, when I was properly dry, and the varnish of my complexion thoroughly hardened and like enamel, Mr Sprat took me down—examined me all over for the last time— and then, nodding his head to himself several times, with a face of seriousness and satisfaction, as much as to say, "You are a doll fit in all respects for the most polished society,"—he handed me to his wife, who wrapped me up in silver paper, all but the head, and laying me in a basket among nine others papered up in the same way, she carried me off to a large doll-shop not far from the corner of New Turnstile in High Holborn.

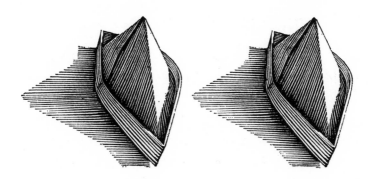

CHAPTER II.

MY FIRST MAMMA.

I arrived safe at the doll-shop, and Mrs Sprat took me out of the basket with her finger and thumb, keeping all her other fingers spread out, for fear of soiling my silver paper.

"Place all these dolls on the shelf in the back parlour," said the master of the shop. "I have no room yet for them in the window." As I was carried to the shelf I caught a glimpse of the shop-window! What a bright and confused sensation it gave me! Everything seemed so light and merry and numerous! And then, through all this crowd of many shapes and colours, packed and piled and hanging up in the window, I saw the crowds of large walking people passing outside in the world, which was as yet perfectly unknown to

me! Oh how I longed to be placed in the shop-
window! I felt I should learn things so fast, if I
could only see them. But I was placed in a dark
box, among a number of other dolls, for a long time,
and when I was taken out I was laid upon my
back upon a high shelf, with my rosy cheeks and
blue eyes turned towards the ceiling.

Yet I cannot say that the time I passed on this
shelf was by any means lost or wasted. I thought
of all I had seen in Mr Sprat's room, and all I had
heard them talk about, which gave me many very
strange and serious thoughts about the people who
lived in the world only for the purpose, as I supposed, of buying dolls. The conversation of Mr
Sprat with his family made me very naturally think
this; and in truth I have never since been quite able
to fancy but that the principal business of mankind
was that of buying and selling dolls and toys.
What I heard the master of the shop in Holborn
often say, helped to fix this early impression on
my mind.

But the means by which I learned very much of
other things and other thoughts, was by hearing the
master's little girl Emmy read aloud to her elder
sister. Emmy read all sorts of pretty books, every
word of which I eagerly listened to, and felt so much

interested, and so delighted, and so anxious and curious to hear more. She read pretty stories of little boys and girls, and affectionate mammas and aunts, and kind old nurses, and birds in the fields and woods, and flowers in the gardens and hedges; and then such beautiful fairy tales; and also pretty stories in verse; all of which gave me great pleasure, and were indeed my earliest education. There was the lovely book called 'Birds and Flowers,' by Mary Howitt; the nice stories about 'Willie,' by Mrs Marcet; the delightful little books of Mrs Harriet Myrtle,—in which I did *so* like to hear about old Mr Dove, the village carpenter, and little Mary, and the account of May Day, and the Day in the Woods,—and besides other books, there was oh! *such* a story-book called 'The Good-natured Bear'![1] But I never heard any stories about dolls, and what they thought, or what happened to them! This rather disappointed me. Living at a doll-shop, and hearing the daughter of the master of such a wonderful shop reading so often, I naturally expected to have heard more about dolls than any other creatures! However, on the whole, I was very well contented, and should have been perfectly happy if they would only have hung me up in the shop window! What I wanted was to be placed in the bright window, and to look into the astonishing street!

Soon after this, however, by a fortunate accident, I was moved to an upright position with my back against a doll's cradle, so that I could look down into the room below, and see what was going on there.

How long I remained upon the shelf I do not know, but it seemed like years to me, and I learned a great deal.

One afternoon Emmy had been reading to her sister as usual, but this time the story had been about a great Emperor in France, who, once upon a time, had a great many soldiers to play with, and whose name was Napoleon Bonaparte.[2] The master himself listened to this, and as he walked thoughtfully up and down from the back room to the shop in front, he made himself a cock'd hat of brown paper, and put it upon his head, with the corners pointing to each shoulder. Emmy continued to read, and the master continued thoughtfully walking up and down with his hands behind him, one hand holding the other.

But presently, and when his walk had led him into the front shop, where I could not see him, the shop-bell rang and Emmy ceased reading. A boy had come in, and the following dialogue took place.

"If you please, sir," said the voice of the boy, "do you want a nice Twelfth-cake?"[3]

"Not particularly," answered the master, "but I have no objection to one."

"What will you give for it, sir?" said the boy.

"That is quite another question," answered the master; "go about your business. I am extremely engaged."

"I do not want any money for it, sir," said the boy.

"What do you mean by that, my little captain?" said the master.

"Why, sir," said the boy, "if you please I want a nice doll for my little sister, and I will give you this large Twelfth-cake that I have in paper here for a good doll."

"Let me see the cake," said the master. "So, how did you get this cake?"

"My grandfather is a pastry-cook, sir," answered the boy, "and my sister and I live with him. I went to-day to take home seven Twelfth-cakes. But the family at one house had all gone away out of the country, and locked up the house, and forgotten to send for the cake; and grandfather told me that I and my sister might have it."

"What is your name?"

"Thomas Plummy, sir; and I live in Bishopsgate street, near the Flower Pot."[4]

"Very well, Thomas Plummy; you may choose any doll you fancy out of that case."

Here some time elapsed; and while the boy was choosing, the master continued his slow walk to and fro from one room to the other, with the brown paper cock'd hat, which he had forgotten to take off, still upon his head. It was so very light that he did not feel it, and did not know it was there. At last the boy declared he did not like any of the dolls in the case, and so went from one case to another, always refusing those the master offered him; and when he did choose one himself the master said it was too expensive. Presently the master said he had another box full of good dolls in the back room, and in he came, looking so grave in his cock'd hat, and beginning to open a long wooden box. But the boy had followed him to the door, and peeping in suddenly, called out, "There, sir! that one! that is the doll for my cake!" and he pointed his little brown finger up at me.

"Aha!" said the master, "that one is also too expensive; I cannot let you have that."

However, he took me down, and while the boy

was looking at me with evident satisfaction, as if his mind was quite made up, the master got a knife and pushed the point of it into the side of the cake, just to see if it was as good inside as it seemed to be on the outside. During all this time he never once recollected that he had got on the brown-paper cock'd hat.

"Now," said the master, taking me out of the boy's hand, and holding me at arm's length, "you must give me the cake and two shillings besides for this doll. This is a young lady of a very superior make, is this doll. Made by one of the first makers. The celebrated Sprat, the only maker, I may say, of these kind of jointed dolls. See! all the joints move —all work in the proper way; up and down, backwards and forwards, any way you please. See what lovely blue eyes; what rosy cheeks and lips; and what a complexion on the neck, face, hands, and arms! The hair is also of the most beautiful kind of delicate light-brown curl that can possibly be found. You never before saw such a doll, nor any of your relations. It is something, I can tell you, to have such a doll in a family; and if you were to buy her, she would cost you a matter of twelve shillings!"

The boy, without a moment's hesitation, took the

cake and held it out flat upon the palm of his hand, balancing it as if to show how heavy it was.

"Sir," said he, "this is a Twelfth-cake, of very superior make. If the young lady who sits reading there was only to taste it, she would say so too. It was made by my grandfather himself, who is known to be one of the first makers in all Bishops-gate street: I may say the very first. There is no better in all the world. You see how heavy it is; what a quantity of plums, currants, butter, sugar, and orange and lemon-peel there is in it, besides brandy and carraway comfits. See! what a beautiful frost-work of white sugar there is all over the top and sides! See, too, what characters there are, and made in sugar of all colours! Kings and Queens in their robes, and lions and dogs, and Jem Crow, and Swiss cottages in winter, and railway carriages, and girls with tambourines, and a village steeple with a cow looking in at the porch; and all these standing or walking, or dancing upon white sugar, surrounded with curling twists and true lover's knots in pink and green citron, with damson cheese and black currant paste between. You never saw such a cake before, sir, and I'm sure none of your family ever smelt any cake at all like it. It's quite a nosegay for the Queen Victoria herself; and if you were to buy it at grandfather's shop you would have to pay fifteen shillings and more for it."

"Thomas Plummy!" said the master, looking very earnestly at the boy; "Thomas Plummy! take the doll, and give me the cake. I only hope it may prove half as good as you say. And it is my opinion that, if you, Thomas Plummy, should not happen to be sent to New South Wales to bake brown bread, you may some day or other come to be Lord Mayor of London."

"Thank you, sir," said the boy. "How many Abernethy biscuits will you take for your cock'd hat?"

The master instantly put his hand up to his head, looking so confused and vexed, and the boy ran laughing out of the shop. At the door he was met by his sister, who had been waiting to receive me in her arms: and they both ran home, the little girl hugging me close to her bosom, and the boy laughing so much at the affair of the cock'd hat that he could hardly speak a word all the way.

CHAPTER III.

TWELFTH-NIGHT.

———◆———

That evening little Ellen Plummy begged to go to bed much earlier than usual. She took me with her, and I had the great happiness of passing the whole night in the arms of my first mamma.

The next morning, however, was the day before Twelfth-day, and there were so many preparations to be made, and so many things to do in the house, that the pastry-cook required the help of every body who could do anything at all; so he desired Ellen to put me in a box till Twelfth-night was over, because he wanted her to sort small cakes, and mix sugar plums of different colours, and pile up sticks of barley sugar, and arrange artificial flowers, and stick bits of holly with red berries into cakes for the upper shelves of his shop window.

I was, therefore, placed in a dark box in the bedroom, and lay there thinking.

After I had gone over in my mind all that I had at present seen and heard since I was a doll, I began to wonder how long this confinement in the dark box would continue. The morning seemed so very long. But twice my little mamma, Ellen, came creeping softly up stairs, and ran and opened the box—took me out, gave me a kiss, put me in again, shut the lid of the box, and down stairs she softly tripped back, to continue her work. The afternoon was also terribly long, and I saw nothing of mamma till about six in the evening, when she came and took me out, and embraced me, and said, "Oh you dear doll! I shall come to put you to bed!" and away she ran again.

About nine o'clock mamma came and took me out of my box. She had contrived to find time in the course of the day to make, in a very hasty manner, a little night-gown and night-cap for me, which she immediately put on me, and then took me to bed with her as before.

Next morning was Twelfth-day, and I was again

placed in the dark box. Ellen had so much to do
that all this day she was quite unable to come
even once to take a peep at me. Oh how long
the dark day was! and how tired I felt of it! However,
I was obliged to be as patient as I could, and tried
to amuse myself with my own thoughts and
recollections.

I called to mind the poor dusky room where I
was manufactured and born, with its three beds
upon the floor on one side, and the long work-
bench at the other, and all the strange shadows
of the dolls upon the walls by candle-light;
dozens of funny shadows cast from the dolls
that hung upon the lines or stood upon the beams.
And when the candle was moved about these
shadows danced. I also recollected many conversations that had taken place between the celebrated
Mr Sprat and his wife, when the children were asleep
and the candle was out, as to how they should be able
to afford an apple-pie for dinner next Sunday week,
which was the little man's birthday. Then I recollected the many cold dark nights, and days almost as
dull, which I had passed in the box at the doll shop,
before, by a lucky accident, I was moved to an upright
position on the top of the shelf. After that I went
over in my mind all the pretty stories and other

books that had been read by Emmy in the shop.
This made me happier; yet I could not forget the
many dark days and nights in the box. Nor did
I consider my present condition better, and felt
sadly impatient at being thus shut up in a small
box, and quite alone besides, without another doll
to whisper a word to.

I had just begun to get very sad, when suddenly
I heard the sound of little feet tripping over the
floor; the lid of my box was opened, and I saw
a beautiful fairy standing over me! I was taken
out by a pair of soft warm hands, and who should
it be but my mamma, dressed all in white, with silver
bracelets, and roses in her hair, and a bit of most
beautiful violet tinsel stuck upon the breast of her
frock! "Come!" cried she, clasping me in her
arms, "come down stairs with me, you poppet!
you shall come with me, Maria, and see Twelfth-
night!"

Out of the room she ran with me, and down
stairs! The staircase was all lighted with gas! I
was going to see Twelfth-night! and I had that
instant been christened, and my name was Maria
Poppet! Oh how delighted I felt! I tried to jump
out of mamma's arms, I was so pleased—but I
could not; and this was fortunate, because perhaps

I could not have jumped back again. But I felt *so* happy!

She ran straight with me into the very shop itself—the fine front shop with All the Cakes! How shall I describe it? How shall I tell the effect it had upon me? Oh, it is impossible. I fainted away.

When I came to my senses I found that my mamma had placed me upright between two tall, round glass jars, one full of glittering barley-sugar sticks twisted, and the other full of large sugar plums of all colours; and I was close behind the counter where she stood to serve. I saw nothing else distinctly, my eyes were so dazzled, and so indeed were all my senses. Amidst a blaze of gas, crowded with immense cakes, the round white sugar island of each being covered with its extraordinary inhabitants, there was the front window in all its glory! Scenes in eastern countries, with elephants and dromedaries and great palm trees (the names of all which my mamma told me afterwards), and negro people and tigers sitting under orange trees; and scenes in northern countries, where all is snow and frost and tall rocks of ice, and bears walking round broken ships; and scenes in delightful countries, where the weather is so beautiful, and

where people play guitars and sing all day and half
the night, too, in groves and gardens; and scenes in
many parts of England, where the fields are so very
green, and the daisies and buttercups in such thousands and thousands; and wonderful scenes in no
country ever yet discovered, but which were all once
to be seen in fairy-land, if anybody could find
them; these and many more things were all upon
the tops of the large cakes in the lower part of the
window, together with sprigs of holly, oh, so full
of bright red berries!—and here and there shining
blanc-mange and jellies in the shape of baskets of
fruit and flowers, and three round glass bowls full
of gold and silver fish, who constantly moved round,
staring, with their noses pushing against the glass,
in imitation of a crowd of children outside the shop
window, who were all staring and pushing their
noses against the glass in just the same way. There
was a shelf which ran across the middle of the
window, close to the front, and this was also thick
with cakes of a smaller sort, and all covered with
Twelfth-night characters, in coloured sugar; but what
they were it was impossible to see for the glitter of the
beautiful barley-sugar sticks that were piled up in
round glass jars, across and across, and standing
between the cakes. There were also cakes on a

top shelf, near the top of the window, but here scarcely anything could be seen for the blaze of the gas.

In the shop itself there was continually a crowd coming in to buy cakes or other things, for the counter was also covered with delightful wonders, and the old gentleman pastry-cook and great cake-maker himself walked about in the middle of the shop, dressed in his best, with a large red rose in the button-hole of his coat, smiling and rubbing his hands together, and chatting with all the children that came in, and sometimes going to the door and giving a handful of sugar plums to children outside who had no money to buy anything. But behind the counter there were his grown-up niece, and the pretty girl who served in the shop, and his grand-daughter, who was my mamma; and all of these were dressed in white muslin, with borders of lace and bright ribbons. His niece, however, was the most like a princess, for she had a blue satin turban on, with feathers hanging down over one side, and a silk scarf with gold fringe edges, and a red cor-nelian necklace, with beads as large as turnip radishes.

I bore all this extraordinary scene as long as I could, until at last, out of too much happiness, I

was unable to endure it any longer, and then something happened to me. I felt my eyes twink and
twitch and wink, and feel a little sore; and without
knowing it, or knowing anything, except that I was
in a state of the most indescribable happiness, I fell
fast asleep.

CHAPTER IV.

THE LITTLE MILLINERS.

My life at the pastrycook's passed in a very pleasant manner; but not because of the cakes or pastry. For, in the first place, every night was not like Twelfth-night; and as for the pastry, though I was delighted to see it for some time, and to notice how much it was admired and longed for, yet in the course of a few weeks I had seen so many little girls and boys make themselves unwell by eating too many raspberry tarts and cheesecakes, that I almost ceased to take any farther interest in those things. My eyes were constantly employed in observing the different people who came in and out, or passed by the door and window; my ears were constantly attentive to all that was said; and my mind was busily engaged in thinking over all I had seen, and all I had heard, both spoken and read from books, ever since I was a doll. By these means I advanced my education very much, because my memory became stronger by practice, and my understanding was improved by this habit of thinking over everything to myself. I believe no doll ever lived who was more anxious to learn and know about all sorts of things—good, pretty, or wonderful—than I was.

I soon had an opportunity of seeing a very different set of things from the cakes, and tarts, and buns, and sugar plums. We left our abode at the pastry-cook's. Ellen Plummy was sent to be a milliner to her aunt, who employed a great number of girls in making ladies' dresses. Ellen was only seven years old, and she cried at leaving her kind grandfather's; but he kissed her, and told her he knew it would be best for her, so she dried her eyes and tried to look cheerful: and her brother Thomas carried her little grey box. She carried me herself in her arms.

Her Aunt Sharpshins was a very tall, thin, pale-faced woman, who was always dressed in a long

gown made close up to the throat, of the colour of
old nankeen, with a faded bed-furniture pattern
round the hem at the bottom. She had a nose like
a parrot's beak, and always spoke through it. She
kept fifteen little milliner girls in the house, who
were her apprentices, and obliged to work as long
as she pleased. The youngest was about ten years
of age; her name was Nanny Bell, and she and
my mamma Ellen became great friends directly.

Now this tall Aunt Sharpshins, with the parrot's
nose, made her fifteen little milliners all work together in the same room, all seated upon small
chairs without backs, so that they could not lean
backward to rest themselves. And she made
them work the whole day, from six o'clock in the
morning till eight o'clock at night, with only about
half an hour's rest at one o'clock, when they were
all called down stairs to dinner in the back parlour
of the house. Some of the poor girls often cried, or
fell asleep and tumbled off their chairs, they were so
tired. If this misfortune happened to them, Mrs
Sharpshins used to give them only bread and water
for dinner; and sometimes she was so cruel as even to
give them a loud slap on the shoulders.

One day my mamma Ellen and Nanny Bell were
sitting alone together in the back parlour after

dinner, to talk a little, as Aunt Sharpshins had gone out to take some dresses home. "Ah," said Ellen, "I do so wish to go back to my grandfather's, he was such a kind pastry-cook; and my brother Tom was so very fond of me always. I am so sorry to be a milliner; and although my aunt says I am to be her partner, perhaps, when I grow up, yet I do not like it."

"But then," said Nanny Bell, "you would be much kinder to all of us than your aunt is. You would not make us work so long every day, would you? and have so little rest, would you, Ellen? and such poor, cold dinners, with not enough either —now, would you?"

"*That* I would not!" exclaimed Ellen, giving me a toss in the air with both hands, "*that* I would not! You should only work as long as I worked myself; and when I was tired, then I should know that all of you must be tired, and I should say, 'Now let's go down stairs, and have each a large slice of cake.' Then, in the evening, as soon as it was dark, and we began to feel our eyes sore with looking at the work, we would again go down stairs, and all have tea together, and after that a dance; and we would dance reels, and jigs, and hornpipes, and quadrilles, but mostly reels.—Hark! Aunt Sharpshins is ringing at the door!" And away the two little girls ran scampering up stairs; and in her haste and terror Ellen gave my head such a knock against the banisters! But she was so sorry, and kissed me so often to make it well.

Up to this time I had never been properly dressed; for, excepting a strip of bright blue ribbon round my waist, and a small cap of purple silk stuck on the back of my head, I was in the very same long white night-gown which Ellen had made for me when I first went to the pastry-cook's house, and in which I made my first appearance in the shop among all the gas-lights and cakes on Twelfth-night. So my dear mamma and Nanny Bell determined to make me a proper dress.

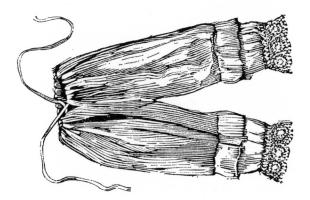

CHAPTER V.

MY FIRST FROCK AND TROUSERS.

———◆———

There were plenty of little odds and ends of silks, and stuffs, and velvets, and muslins, which Ellen had already collected, and which her aunt had told her she might have; and with these they knew they could make me a beautiful dress. They finished their dinner as fast as possible, and ran up stairs again, in order to be alone for this pleasant work.

They accordingly began by carefully measuring me round the waist and round the shoulders; and then across the back down to the waist, measuring from the right shoulder crossing down to the middle of the left side, and from the left shoulder across to the middle of the right side. Their little fingers were busy about me in all directions: they did so tickle me!

Then they measured my arms; first from the top of the shoulder to the elbow when bent, and next from the tip of the elbow to the wrist. Lastly, they measured me from the back of my neck down to the middle of the waist, just where there is, or ought to be, the most bend in a doll's back; and from this they measured for the skirt right down below my knees, and for the trousers they measured down as low as my ankles.

But how were these two little girls to find time to do all this work for me? The whole day they were engaged, from six o'clock in the morning till bed time. So, as it was now summer, and quite light at five o'clock, Ellen and Nanny both determined to get up at that time, and thus have an hour every morning to themselves, in order to make me a frock and trousers. And they calculated that by doing this for a week, they could easily finish the task they had set themselves.

But the poor little girls had to work so hard for more than thirteen hours every day, that neither of them could awake in time. After several mornings, however, Ellen did manage to wake up enough to speak, and call Nanny; and Nanny woke up enough just to answer. After which down sunk their cheeks upon the pillow, and they were fast asleep in a moment.

The next morning Nanny Bell called Ellen at about half-past five o'clock, and Ellen made a great effort, and sat up in bed with her eyes shut. At last she half opened one eye, and then she saw poor Nanny as fast asleep again as if she had never called her. So, back fell Ellen upon her pillow.

Now, for several nights they both made great resolutions before they went to sleep; but when the morning came they could not keep them, though they tried very much to do so; and one morning Ellen, directly that Nanny called her, rolled herself out of bed upon the floor. But there she lay, and when the other girls were going past the door to their work at six o'clock, and came in to see if Ellen and Nanny were dressed, there they found Ellen fast asleep upon the floor in her night-gown.

Something, however, happened in consequence of this. Ellen had caught a bad cold and sore throat with sleeping upon the floor, and the doctor said she must remain in bed for two days to get rid of it. Ellen was, therefore, sent to bed again soon after dinner, and as it was necessary that somebody should be with her to give her medicine, or barley water to drink, Nanny Bell was chosen by her own request. Here was a chance! Now was the time to work at my frock and trousers.

But there was something to be done first. There was physic to be taken. It was brought by Aunt Sharpshins in a tea-cup, and it had a dark red and yellow colour, and oh, such a strong smell! Poor Ellen looked at her aunt so pitifully, as much as to say "Must I really take this nasty physic?" —then she looked into the tea-cup, and made a face—then she looked round the room making the same face, only sadder—then she gave a little frown as much as to say "Why should I be afraid? I know it is good for me—I am determined to take it!" then she shut her eyes—put the tea-cup to her lips—and down went the physic!

As soon as Mrs Sharpshins left them, Nanny produced some sugar plums out of a little paper for Ellen to take after her medicine; and as they ate the sugar plums, Nanny laughed at the horrid faces my mamma had made before she took her physic and just after it was down, and then they both laughed very much.

Ellen now sat up in bed, and Nanny helped her to prop herself up with pillows at her back, and covered her shoulders with a large shawl. Nanny then brought all the bits of muslin, and silk, and stuffs, and velvet, together with a pair of scissors, and needles and thread, and spread them out upon the quilt before Ellen. I was placed on the bed beside her with my head raised high, so that I might see them working. When all was ready, Nanny got upon the bed and sat down opposite to Ellen, and to work they both went.

The measurements had already been made, and the slips of paper with the marks were laid upon the quilt. Then they began cutting out. First they cut out my under-clothes, and these were all of cambric muslin, which they said was necessary, in order to be soft to the skin of such a little creature as I was. I could not help laughing to myself when I heard them say this, because I was made all of wood, and my skin was only the fine hard polished varnish of the celebrated Mr Sprat. I was not quite so tender as they fancied. They next cut me out a small under-bodice of white jean instead of stays. Then came the trousers, which were cut long and full, and were of soft white muslin trimmed with open work. Then they cut out a petticoat of fine cambric muslin, the body quite tight and the skirt very full all round. My frock was made to fit nicely to the shape, but not too tight. It was of fine lemon-coloured merino, with a sash of violet-coloured velvet, and very full in the skirt, and they said it must have some stiff muslin inside the hem to make it set out, and not hang too loosely in the folds.

When all was cut out and arranged, my mamma and Nanny both went to work with their needles, and they worked all the day as long as they could see. The under-clothes and the trousers were all quite finished, and the body and one sleeve of the frock was begun.

The next morning, after my mamma had taken her medicine and made the same horrid face as before, only not quite so bad this time, they went to work again. But this second morning the weather was not so warm as the day before, so Nanny went to the bed of one of the other girls and took off the top sheet, and tied up a bit of it in the middle with a long and strong tape in a strong knot, and then with a chair upon the bed she managed to tie the other end to a nail in the wall just over the head of the bed; she then spread out all the sheet that hung down so as to cover them both in, like a little tent. And in this pleasant manner they worked all the second day, by which time my frock was quite finished.

Besides this they had made me a pair of silk stockings, which were sewed upon my legs to make them fit better; and as I was naturally from my birth rather

stiff in the ankles and instep, they made the stockings without feet, but sewed black satin over both my
feet in the shape of the prettiest boots possible, with
stitches of cross work in front. When all was done,
and everything put upon me, nothing would do but
they must take me out for a walk round the room.

Out we all got from the tent; my mamma in her
night-gown and shawl, with a bit of flannel round
her throat, and list shoes, and I walking between
the two little girls, each holding me by the hand.
But we had hardly walked twice round the room,
talking like ladies who are out in the park, when
suddenly we heard Aunt Sharpshins coming up
stairs! In a moment we were all upon the bed—
down came the tent—underneath the bed it was
thrown—into the bed we all three got as quick as
possible—and when Mrs Sharpshins came into the
room we all seemed fast asleep!

She stood at the foot of the bed, looking at us.
After a minute or two she went down again.

"How you laughed and shook the bed," said my
mamma to Nanny. "I thought she would have
found us out, and somehow I wish she had. I don't
like to have pretended to be asleep."

"But," answered Nanny, "she would have been so
unkind if she had seen us walking in the park."

"I wish people would not be unkind," sighed my mamma; and then she added, "How dear and kind *you* are, Nanny; and how you have worked for me, and nursed me all these two days!"

At this they threw their arms round each other's necks, and so we all three went to sleep in reality, quite forgetting the tent which had been thrown under the bed. But it was a good-natured, merry girl that it belonged to, and she only gave my mamma and Nanny a good tickling when she found it, after a long search, at bed-time.

CHAPTER VI.

THE LITTLE LADY.

My mamma got quite well as soon as my frock and trousers were finished; and whenever she was allowed to go out with her aunt she took me with her. The girl whose sheet had been taken for the tent had made me a scarf of violet-coloured satin, and a white silk bonnet, and these I always had on when we went out.

In a few weeks, however, I was destined to lose this kind mamma, and become the dear doll of another. If I could have foreseen that this would happen I should have fretted very much, because I was so fond of Ellen Plummy.

But it did happen, and in this manner.

One fine summer's day Mrs Sharpshins took Ellen for a walk in St James's park, and after a little time we came to the piece of water, and saw several pretty children feeding the swans that live in that water. The children had some bread and small buns, which they broke in little pieces and threw into the water, where they floated till the swans swam up to the bread and bent their long white necks down to eat it. Ellen begged her aunt to let her stay and look at the swans. "Look, Maria!" said she to me, "what beautiful, bright, black eyes they have, and what lovely snow-white necks, and how gracefully the breast of the swan moves upon the water, while the necks are in the shape of a beautiful arch!"

While they were looking at the swans, a very tall footman, in a green and gold livery, with a long golden-headed cane and powdered hair, came up to Mrs Sharpshins from a carriage that was waiting near at hand, in which sat a grown-up lady with a little lady by her side. Both of them had also been observing the swans; but in doing so the little lady had at the same time fixed her eyes on me.

"The Countess of Flowerdale wishes to speak with you," said the footman to Mrs Sharpshins. Now the countess was a great lady, who sometimes

employed Aunt Sharpshins to make her dresses for
the country and to walk in the garden. We went
with the footman, and I could see that Mrs Sharpshins was in a great agitation.

"Mrs Sharpshins," said the countess, smiling, and
with a gentle voice, "this young lady has been looking at your little girl's doll more than at the swans,
and she has taken a great fancy to the doll. The
little girl is your niece, I believe. Will she part with
her doll? I shall be glad to purchase it or send her
another."

"Oh, anything your ladyship wishes, of course,"
said Mrs Sharpshins, with a very low curtsey.

"Would you like to part with your doll, my dear?"
said the lady to Ellen.

I felt Ellen give me such a close hug, as much
as to say, "Oh, no, no!" But her aunt stooped
down and looked in her face under her bonnet with
such a look! The great lady did not see it, but I
saw it.

"I could not think of taking it from your little
niece if she is indisposed to part with it," said the
great lady in a sweet voice.

Upon this the small lady by her side, who seemed
to be about eight years of age, turned red in the
face—the corners of her mouth dropped down—her

eyes grew large and round, and out rolled one large proud tear. But she did not cry, or say a word.

Whether it was this one silent tear of the little lady, or the sweet voice of the great lady, or the look that her aunt had given her under her bonnet, I do not know, but Ellen, first giving me a kiss, lifted me up towards the carriage window, and gave me into the hands of the little lady with such a sigh!

"Thank you, my dear," said the great lady. "I will take care to send you another handsome doll and doll's cradle to-morrow morning, and something besides; and Mrs Sharpshins, you can make me three or four more morning dresses the same as the last. I am in no hurry for them."

The very tall footman got up to his place behind the carriage—the carriage drove off; the great lady nodded to Ellen; the little lady kissed her white glove to her; and Mrs Sharpshins made a low curtsey, taking care to step just before Ellen in order that they should not see the tears that were just beginning to gush out of her eyes.

My new mamma, the little Lady Flora, was very pretty. She had a complexion like the most delicate wax-work, large bright eyes, a dimple in each cheek, and dimples all over her little knuckles. She had taken off her gloves to arrange my hair better, and began at once to talk to me in a very delightful manner.

We drove from St James's park into Hyde park, and on the way we passed a very great doll indeed, but looking so cross and black, and without any clothes on. "Look there, dear!" said my little lady mamma, "that is the strongest and largest doll ever seen in London. His name is 'Achilles,'—and the ladies of London had him made of iron and brass, because the Duke of Wellington was so lucky in playing at ball on the fields of Waterloo!" [5] The countess seemed much amused with this account. We met a great number of elegant carriages on our way, and nearly all the ladies inside exchanged salutations with the countess, and nodded to my little lady mamma. All who were elegant, and richly dressed, and beautiful, and in fine carriages with rich liveries, seemed to know each other, and all to be upon such delightful terms of affectionate intimacy! "Oh!" thought I, "here is a new world! Everybody seems to respect, and admire, and love everybody else! How very delightful!"

CHAPTER VII.

THE WEST END OF THE TOWN.

———◆———

Our house was in Hanover square, a few doors from the Queen's Concert Rooms.[6] There happened to be a morning concert on the first day of my arrival, and as one of the drawing-room windows where I sat with my little lady mamma opened out upon the balcony, we could every now and then hear the trumpets and drums, and one violin which squeaked so sweetly high above all the rest.

At four o'clock my new mamma went out for a drive in her carriage with her governess, and chiefly to buy several things for me. Of course I went too.

First we drove to pay a visit to a young lady in Grosvenor square, and after this we drove to a toy-shop in Oxford street,[7] and there the little Lady Flora bought me a cradle of delicate white basket work, with a mattress and pillow covered with cotton of pale pink and lilac stripes. She wanted a feather-bed; but they had not got one. The governess then bought a large, handsome doll, chosen by Lady Flora, to send to my dear first mamma, Ellen Plummy, in exchange for me, and also a nice cradle, and one or two other things which I did not see.

We next went down Regent street, and sent the very tall footman with the gold-headed cane and powdered hair into every shop that seemed likely, to ask if they had a doll's feather-bed. But none of them had. One young person, however, dressed in black, with a pale face, and her hair very nicely plaited, came out to the carriage window and said, "They would be most happy to *make* a feather-bed for the doll, if her ladyship would allow them that honour!" My little lady mamma, however, said, "Certainly not—I thank you."

We passed the Regent's quadrant, after sending into two or three shops, and then turned up Picca-dilly, and got out at the Burlington arcade. But no such thing as a doll's feather-bed could be found. The little lady, however, bought me a small gold watch and chain, which cost a shilling. We then

returned to the carriage, drove down Waterloo
place, and sent into several shops to inquire, while
we slowly drove towards the Duke of York's
column.[8] My lady mamma explained to me that
the black doll on the top was once a great duke,
who was at the head of all the army when he was
alive, in the same way that he was now at the top of
that fine column. The very tall footman presently
returned, saying he was very sorry to inform Lady
Flora that he had not been so fortunate as to
discover a doll's feather-bed at any of the shops; so
we turned round and drove up Bond street, and tried
at several shops with no better success; then we
passed again down Oxford street, and went to the
Soho Bazaar.[9]

There, at the top of a long room—on the left-
hand side—in a corner—there, at last, we did find
a doll's feather-bed, and of a very superior quality.
No doll in the world, and particularly a wooden
doll, could have wished for anything softer. At the
same place were also many articles of furniture,
such as dolls of the higher class are accustomed to
have, and some of these were bought for me. That
which I was most pleased with was a doll's wardrobe made of cedar wood, with drawers for clothes
in the middle, and pegs to hang dresses upon at

each side, and all enclosed with folding doors, and smelling so sweet. All of these things being carefully packed up in silver paper, and then placed one upon the other, were given to the very tall footman with powdered hair, who receiving them with a serious face, and carrying them balanced on the palm of one hand, and holding up his long gold-headed cane in the other, slowly walked behind us, with his chin raised high out of his white neck-cloth, to the admiration of everybody in the bazaar, as we returned to our carriage.

We now drove once more into Regent street, to a pastry-cook's, and there I was left lying upon the seat of the carriage all alone, while Lady Flora and her governess went to have something nice. But I did not care much about this, as my mind was occupied with several thoughts. In the first place, the pastry-cook's window, though very elegant, presented nothing like the brilliant appearance of Mr Plummy's shop-window on Twelfth-night! No —that first impression exceeded anything else of the kind, and was never to be effaced. But there was one other thought that troubled me a little. It was this. I had been accustomed hitherto to think myself not only very pretty, but one of the very nicest and best dolls that could possibly be. I had always understood that the celebrated Mr Sprat, who had made me, was one of the very first doll-makers in England! The master of the doll-shop in Holborn, who had walked to and fro, like Napoleon Bonaparte in a brown-paper cocked hat, had said so in my hearing; and I had believed it. I naturally considered myself a charming doll. But I had seen many other dolls of quite a different make in the Soho Bazaar!—dolls which I could not help fancying were superior to any of those made by poor Mr Sprat, and therefore very superior to myself. This thought hurt my vanity and humbled me. Of course I had been very vain and conceited. What else could you expect of a doll? But now I certainly felt much less vain, for I plainly saw that there were other dolls in the world who were far prettier and better made than myself. However, as I had been already beloved by two mammas, I soon became contented, and felt no jealousy or envy of the prettiness or fineness of others; and I also believed that if I was amiable, and could become clever, I should never be without someone to love me.

My mamma and her governess now returned to the carriage, and we drove home.

CHAPTER VIII.

A NARROW ESCAPE.

———◆———

I had a narrow escape of a most terrible accident a few days after, of a kind which I shall never forget as long as I live. As it happened at the close of a day on which I saw several new things, I may as well give a short account of that day, and finish with my narrow escape.

The carriage was ordered at twelve o'clock, and we drove to the Regent's park. I had on a new bonnet with a white lace veil, and looked very nice. After driving once round the circle, we got out at the Zoological Gardens,[10] and went in to see the animals.

My little lady mamma first took me to see the parrots, and parroquets, and macaws. Some of the macaws were all white; some white, with an orange-coloured top-knot; some were green, with scarlet and blue in the wings and tail, and with scarlet and white in their faces. Then they had two or three very long, straight feathers in their tails, and they spoke to each other, and often scolded in a very hoarse voice. Some of the parrots were all green, some all grey; but there was one of the parroquets—a little bright-eyed, quick fellow,—who was nearly all red, and had a funny, impudent crown of feathers of white and purple upon the top of his head, but a very short tail. Now, as we were looking at him, Lady Flora suddenly took a fancy to touch his short tail—not with her own hand though, but with mine, which she poked through the wires of his cage for that purpose. "Kark!" cried the little red, quick fellow, turning round very briskly and giving such a peck at my hand. He just missed me, because the governess, who was close by, instantly drew back my mamma's arm, and mine too, of course, at the same time; the peck, however, fell upon the edge of the cage and made a mark in the wood. This was a narrow escape, everybody would say; still it is not the terrible one I shall presently have to relate.

After this, the same little quick fellow pretended his poll wanted scratching, and held down his head to have it done for him, with his eyes shut—one eye, though, not quite close,—and his head turned rather sideways. "No, no!" said the governess, "no thank you, sir; you only want to get another chance of a peck at our fingers!" So we went away, and then the little quick fellow looked up in a moment with such a bright eye, and cried "Kark! skrark!"

After this my mamma took me, all trembling as I was, to see the monkeys. As she remembered the danger I had been in from the red parroquet with the impudent top-knot, Lady Flora did not put either of my hands into any of the cages, but held me up in front of one of them, that I might see the monkeys. Oh, how I wished for a voice to cry "Not so close, mamma! do not hold me so close!"

The monkey who was nearest to the bars was the quietest of them. While the others were running and skipping, and climbing all over the cage, this one sat quite still, with his head bent down and his eyes looking upon the floor; and now and then he looked into the black palm of his little brown hand, with a very grave and earnest face, as if he was considering something about which he was very anxious: when all of a sudden he darted one arm through the bars of his cage, right at my head, and just reached my white veil with his little brown hand! He tore it quite off from the bonnet—ran up the wires in front, squeaking and chattering—and the next moment we saw him at the back of the cage, high up, sitting upon a small shelf tearing my veil all to pieces, and showing us his white teeth, with round staring eyes, and his mouth opening and shutting as fast as possible.

This also was a narrow escape, everybody will say; still it is not the terrible one I shall almost directly have to relate.

We went to see the tigers and leopards, and while the governess was looking at a zebra, we went too close to be safe, and also too close to the bars of the elephant's enclosure, so that he could have reached us very well with his trunk; but none of these chances are like the terrible escape I am *now* about to relate. I may well call it a terrible one, because I might have broken my neck or my back, or both, besides breaking the head of somebody else at the same moment.

We drove to the Edgeware road, and down Park lane to Mayfair, in order to pay a visit to a lady of high rank, the Duchess of Guineahen; and then straight home. After Lady Flowerdale, my mamma's mamma, had dined, I heard with the greatest delight that her ladyship intended to take Lady Flora with her this evening to the Italian Opera.[11] Lady Flowerdale had often before said that she thought my mamma was at present too young to go to any place where the hours are always so late; however, she determined to take her.

There was a great fuss in dressing both Lady Flora and myself, but at last it was finished, and we were all impatience to go. I had on a new pink silk frock, with a white lace scarf, and a lovely bouquet of the sweetest flowers was placed in my sash. When we got into the carriage Lady Flowerdale sat on one side, and my mamma and I on the other. We seemed all silks, and muslins, and sparkles, and feathers, and appeared quite to fill the carriage, so that there was not room for another doll.

Out we got, and passed through the crowd and the soldiers at the door, and up stone steps we went, and through passages full of silks, and muslins, and lace, and jewels, and feathers, and chattering— and up more steps, and along more passages, till at last we were in a little box, and looked round into a great place full of little boxes, and deep down upon a crowd below;—and all the place was full of light, and the same kind of silks, and muslins, and lace, and sparkles, and feathers, and chattering, as we had found in the passages and on the stairs, all of which we saw better on account of the dark coats of the gentlemen, who were like the shadows of this picture of a house of fine ladies.

Lady Flora was placed near the edge of the box, as this was her first visit to the Opera. She held me in her arms with my head hanging a little over the edge. Oh, how frightened I was as I looked down! The height was dreadful! There were indeed many rows above us, but there were two below us, and it looked a terrible distance down into the crowd at the bottom. "Oh," cried I to myself, "if my mamma *would* but hold me tighter—I am so frightened!"

Well, the opera commenced, and it was very long. My little lady mamma got quite tired and sleepy before it was half over, and continually asked when the dancing would begin. But the opera still went on, and I saw with alarm that her eyes grew very heavy, and every now and then were shut.

I saw in another box very near us another little lady of about my mamma's age, who had an opera glass in her hand, and was also leaning over the edge of the box; and I thought, "Now if that small lady drops the opera glass upon the head of some gentleman below in the pit, it will only knock a bit of his head off; but if my small lady drops me, I shall be knocked *all* to pieces!"

I had scarcely finished this reflection when, to my indescribable alarm, I felt the hand that held me get looser and looser. Lady Flora was fast asleep!

What feelings, what thoughts, were mine at that moment, I cannot say, for everything within me seemed mingled in confusion with everything that was round me, and I did not know one thing from another. The hand that held me got still looser!

Oh dear me!—how shall I proceed? It was a moment, as the poet Henry Chorley observes—

"When all that's feeble squeaks within the soul!"[12]

The next moment I felt all was over with me! The hand of my sleeping mamma opened—and down,—down I fell into the dark pit below!

As my head was of solid wood and heavy, I fell head foremost; but, most fortunate to relate, the gentleman who was just underneath was holding up his hat, which was a new one, in order to prevent its being crushed by the crowd, and I fell straight into it,—with such a thump, however, that I half knocked out the crown, and my head poked through a great crack on one side.

I was brought up to the box again by somebody —I had not sufficiently recovered to know anything more, except that my little lady mamma was still asleep, and now lay upon a small sofa at the back of the box, covered over with a large French shawl. This, I think I may say, is having had a narrow escape.

CHAPTER IX.

DOLL'S LETTERS.

———◆———

I had the next day a great joy. It was the arrival
of a letter from my dear Ellen Plummy, which
her brother Thomas had brought and given to one
of the housemaids, saying it was a "doll's letter".
The housemaid had given it to a page, and the
page had given it to the tall footman, and he—
after some consideration—had taken it to the
governess, who, having opened it, and read it, and
shown it to Lady Flowerdale, had asked my little
lady mamma if she would allow me to receive a
letter, as one had been sent for me by the little
girl from whom she had received me. Lady Flora
was at first going to say "No," but suddenly she

recollected the sad face of poor Ellen when she placed me in her hands, and then she said "Oh yes!—I should so like to read it." This was the letter. It was addressed on the outside to "Maria Poppet".

"My dearest Maria,

"I have never forgotten you, though I have got another doll; and often when I love this other doll, I am thinking of it as if you were this. I have also had a cradle sent me by the kind great lady and little lady both, and some things for the bedding, and a necklace of beads for myself, besides a small painted workbox. We get up at six o'clock to work as usual, and go to bed at nine, after bread and butter. I am so glad to think you are happy and comfortable, and that you have no hard needlework to do, and the little lady is fond of you. Don't you remember the Twelfth-cake my brother Tommy gave for you, and how he laughed all the way we ran home at something that had happened in the doll shop about Bonaparte and Abernethy biscuits? I often think of you. I never forget you, nor all who have been good to me, and whom I love, and I hope we may some day meet again; and I also hope that your happy life among all the riches of the

world will not make you quite forget your poor first
mamma.

"Your affectionate

"ELLEN PLUMMY."

The little Lady Flora and the governess were
rather amused with this letter of my poor dear
Ellen's, but Lady Flowerdale was very much pleased
with it, and said that, however simple or foolish
it might seem, it showed a good and affectionate
nature in the little girl who had sent it; and she
was of opinion that the doll should write an answer.

This idea of my writing an answer greatly delighted Lady Flora, and she and her governess
sat a whole morning thinking what to say, and
writing upon a slate, and then rubbing it out because it would not do. At the same time the governess was obliged to put a pen very often into my hand,
and teach me to write, and she often seemed so
vexed and tired; but Lady Flora would never let
her rest, so that I really had in this manner an
excellent lesson in writing.

At last a letter, in answer, was composed on a
slate by the governess, with Lady Flora's assistance,
and then a pen was put into my hand by the
governess, so that I wrote the letter. It was then

sent to Lady Flowerdale, to know if she approved of it; but she did not: she said it wanted ease and simplicity, and was not what a nursery letter ought to be, nor like what a doll would say. She then tried herself, but she could not write one to her mind.

That same evening, as she sat at dinner with the earl her husband, they happened to be alone. Lady Flora was gone to bed, but had left me sitting upright in one corner of the room, having forgotten to take me upstairs with her. Her ladyship, observing that Lord Flowerdale, who was a cabinet minister, was troubled with state business, sought to relieve his mind by telling him all about this letter to me, and their difficulty in answering it. The minister at first paid no attention to this triviality, but when her ladyship related how the governess and Lady Flora had tried all the morning to write a proper answer for the doll, and how hard she *herself* had tried, but could not, the minister was amused, and in the end quite laughed, forgot the business of the state, and actually became pleasant. He desired to see the letter. It was brought in by a footman,—placed upon a splendid silver salver, and handed to the minister by the butler with a grave and important face.

The minister read the letter very attentively; then smiled, and laid it by the side of his plate, on which was a slice of currant tart. "So," said he, "Flora and her governess have tried in vain to write a proper reply to this letter from the doll; and your ladyship has also tried in vain. Well, I have a mind to write the reply myself; I need not go down to the house" (meaning, as I afterwards learnt, the House of Lords) "for ten minutes, and if I do not eat this currant tart, but write instead, I can very well spare that time. Bring me my writing-desk."

The desk was brought, and placed on a side-table. His lordship sat down, and opening Ellen Plummy's letter, began to write a reply for me.

He sat with his forehead full of lines, frowning and screwing up his mouth, and working very hard at it, and only writing a few words at a time, after studying Ellen's letter, which lay open before him.

Three times a servant came to announce to his lordship that his carriage was at the door; but he had not finished. At last, however, it was done, and he was about to read it, when, hearing the clock strike, he found he had been three quarters of an hour over it, and, jumping up, hurried out of the room, and I heard the carriage drive off at a great rate.

Lady Flowerdale, with a face of smiling curiosity, told one of the footmen to bring her what his lordship had been writing. She cast her eyes over it, laid it down, and then calmly desired all the servants to leave the room. As soon as they were gone she took it up again hastily, and read it aloud, as if to enjoy it more fully. It was as follows:—

"To Miss E. Plummy.

"Hanover Square, July 15.

"My dear Madam,

"I have the honour to acknowledge the receipt of your very kind letter, the date of which has been omitted, no doubt by an oversight. You have stated that I still hold a place in your memory, although you have now got another doll, and that your affection for this latter one is only by reason of your thoughts dwelling upon me. You have also stated that you possess various little articles; and I, moreover, notice sundry allusions to needlework and Twelfth-cake, to your brother Master Thomas, and to Bonaparte and Mr Abernethy; the purport of which is not necessary for me to discuss. But I must frankly tell you that, having now become the doll of another, I cannot with propriety reciprocate that solicitude which you are pleased to entertain for me, nor can I, for the same reason, address you in similar terms of affection. At the same time, my dear madam, permit me to add that I cherish a lively sense of all the kindness you once showed me, and I cannot doubt of the sincerity of your present professions of respect and esteem.

"I have the honour to be,
"My dear Madam, very faithfully yours,
"M. P."

When the countess had concluded this letter she hastily put a cambric handkerchief up to her face, and particularly over her mouth, and laughed to herself for at least a minute. I also laughed to myself. What a polite, unfeeling, stupid reply to a kind, tender-hearted little girl like Ellen Plummy. Whatever knowledge the minister might have had of grown-up men and women, and the world, and the affairs of state, it was certain he was not equal to enter into the mind of a doll who had a heart like mine. It would have been so *much* better if his lordship, instead of writing that letter, had eaten his currant tart,—and then gone to bed.

Maria Poppet

CHAPTER X.

PLAYING WITH FIRE.

———✦———

I have now something more than a narrow escape to relate; for though I did really escape, yet it was not without a dreadful accident, and some injury. It was also the occasion of my changing my place of residence and style of living. All, however, shall be told in proper order.

Lady Flora having learnt my name from the address of the letter I had received, she took a sudden fancy to have it engraved upon a little gold bracelet. When the bracelet was sent home she fastened it upon my wrist, but it dropped off once or twice, being rather too large, so we drove to the jeweller's house, which was near Charing cross, and there it was fastened to my wrist by rivets, so

that it could not be taken off at all. This was what
Lady Flora desired.

On returning through the Haymarket my mamma
recollected, as we passed the Opera House, that she
had still never seen the dancing there, on account
of her sleeping; and at the same time I, for *my* part,
only recollected my narrow escape. But the loss of
the opera dancing made Lady Flora only think the
more about it, and about dancing; and when we
arrived at home she ran to her mamma, and begged
to be taken to Willis's Rooms—in fact, she wanted
to dance herself at "Almack's,"[13] and to take me
with her, as no doubt there would be many other
dolls in the room, with whom, after mutual and satisfactory introductions, I could associate.

Lady Flowerdale said she was afraid that Lady
Flora, being not yet nine years of age, was too
young to be taken to "Almack's"; she could, however, take her to the Duchess of Guineahen's ball,
which was to be given next month. This greatly
pleased Flora, and meantime she resolved to take an
extra lesson in dancing of Madame Michaud, in
order to be the better prepared for the ball.

I was present at all the lessons of dancing, and
saw Madame Michaud seated with her gold snuff-
box, tapping upon the lid to keep time, and taking

an immense pinch of snuff when Lady Flora danced well, and a still more immense pinch when she danced badly, besides scolding the young man who played the violin, as if it had been his fault.

Another thing, however, and a still more important one, was to be done, before this ball occurred, and this was to get ready the ball dresses. A message was immediately sent to a celebrated milliner in Piccadilly to come immediately and take orders for ball dresses, for Lady Flora and her doll.

During all the time these dresses were being made, my mamma was so impatient and restless that it was quite an unhappiness to see her. I often thought what a pity it was she had not learned to make dresses herself, her mind would then have been employed, and she would have been so much more comfortable. Oh, how different was the happy day I spent among the poor little milliners when Ellen Plummy and Nanny Bell sat under the tent made of a sheet, to make me a frock and trousers. How happy were they over the work, and how impatient and cross was Lady Flora, who had no work to do. Her mind was so disturbed that she was quite unable to attend to any of her lessons; she insisted, however, upon her governess giving me lessons instead, by placing the pen in my hand, and directing it till I had copied several pages of a book. By this means I learned to write,—the governess was employed,—and my mamma said it was the same as if she took her usual lessons.

At last the dresses came home. They were beautiful, and both exactly alike. They were made of the thinnest white gauze, to be worn over very full petticoats of the same white gauze; so that they set out very much, and looked very soft and fleecy. They were trimmed with an imitation of lily of the valley, made in white satin and silver. The trousers were of white satin, trimmed with gauze.

Now there was such a trying on and changing, and proposals for alterations, and sending all back to the milliner's, and having all back again two hours afterwards, to try on once more in case they really did *not* need alteration.

The day of the ball was rather cold and windy; so that, although it was the month of August, a fire was ordered in the nursery, and in Lady Flora's bed-room, lest she might take cold. Towards evening the dresses were all laid out ready to put on; but when my mamma saw them, she could not wait, and insisted upon being dressed, although it was five hours before the time. In two hours and a half she was ready; and then I was dressed, which occupied an hour more. Still there was a long time to wait; so Lady Flora took me in her arms, and began to dance from room to room,—that is, from the nursery to her bed-room, from one fire-place to the other. In doing this she observed that each time she turned, her full, gauze frock gave the fire a *puff*, so that a blaze came; and as she was amused by it, she went each time nearer, and whisked round quicker in order to make the blaze greater. "Oh, Lady Flora!" cried her maid, "pray take care of your dress; you go too near; wait till I run and fetch the fire-guards."

Away ran the maid to fetch the fire-guards; and while she was gone Lady Flora determined to dance for the last time still nearer than ever to each fire before she whisked round. The very next time she did it she went just the least bit too near; the hem of her frock whisked against the bars—and her frock was in a blaze in a moment!

She gave a loud scream and a jump, and was going to run, when most fortunately her foot caught one corner of a thick rug, and down she fell. This smothered the blaze, but still her clothes were on fire; and she lay shrieking and rolling and writhing on the floor.

Up ran the nursery maid, and when she saw

what had happened, she began screaming too—
and up ran the page, and when he saw what had
happened he fell down upon his face with fear and
confusion—and up ran the very tall footman, and
the instant he looked into the room, and smelt
the fire, he ran away again as fast as possible—
and then up ran the countess herself, and she ran
straight to her child, and rolled the thick rug all
round her, and carried her in her arms to her own
room.

Physicians and surgeons were sent for, and all
the burnt things were taken off, and thrown on one
side. Among these I lay; my beautiful dress was
all black tinder; but I was not really much burnt,
nor was Lady Flora. A few weeks might cure her,
though the scars would always remain, and spoil
her prettiness; but what could cure *me*? I was so
scorched and frizzled, that the paint which was on
my skin had blistered and peeled off. I was quite
black. No notice was taken of me; and in the
confusion I was carried out of the room, with the
rest of the burnt rags, and thrown by one of the
servants, in her haste, out of a back window.

How I escaped utter destruction, in this dreadful
fall, I cannot think; unless it was owing to my
being wrapped all round in singed clothes, so that

I fell softly. I had nearly fainted with fear, when the flames first caught my dress; and when the housemaid threw open the window to fling me out, my senses utterly forsook me.

I fell over a low wall, into a passage leading towards some stables. In the course of a few minutes I recovered my senses, but only to experience a fresh alarm! A fine large Newfoundland dog, who was just passing, thought somebody had thrown him a broiled bone; so he caught me up in his mouth, and away he ran with me, wagging his tail.

CHAPTER XI.

THE PORTRAIT PAINTER.

———✦———

The Newfoundland dog soon found that the smell of my burnt clothes and scorched skin was not the same as a broiled bone; and that, in fact, I was not good to eat. But he still continued to hold me in his great warm, red mouth, because he was used to fetch and carry; and, as he felt no wish to taste me, he thought he would take me, just as I was, to his young mistress, who was not far off. He had merely wandered about Hanover square to amuse himself, as he knew the neighbourhood very well.

The dog ran through the door-way of some private stables into a passage that led into the square; and turning down, first one street, then another, he soon stopped at a door, upon which was written, "J. C. Johnson, Portrait Painter."

The door was shut, but the area gate happened to be open; so down ran the dog into the area, and into the front kitchen, and across that to the stairs, and up the stairs (three flights) till he came to the front room of the second floor, which was a-jar, and in he bounced. There sat a little girl and her aunt; and Mr J. C. Johnson was painting the aunt's portrait, in a great white turban.

The dog ran at once to the little girl, and laying me at her feet, sprang back a step or two, and began wagging and swishing his tail about, and hanging out a long crimson tongue, and breathing very fast, and waiting to be praised and patted, and called a good dog, for what he had brought.

"Oh, Nep!" cried the aunt to the dog, "what horrid thing *have* you brought? some dirty old bone."

"It is an Indian idol, I believe," said Mr Johnson, taking me up from the carpet; "an Indian image of ebony, much defaced by time."

"I think," said the little girl, to whom Mr Johnson handed me, "I think it looks very like a wooden doll, with a burnt frock and scorched face."

"Well, so it is, I *do* believe," said the aunt.

"Let me examine the figure once more," said the

portrait-painter, laying down his palette of colours, but keeping his brush in the other hand. "Yes, yes, I fancy, madam, your niece is correct. It is not a work of Indian art, nor of Egyptian, nor of Grecian art; it is the work of a London doll-maker."

I expected he was, of course, about to say, "by the celebrated Mr Sprat," but he did not.

"Oh, you poor London doll!" said the little girl, "what a pity you were not made in India, or some-where a wonderful way off, then Mr Johnson would have taken pity on you, and painted you all over."

Mr Johnson laughed at this; and then gave such a droll look at the little girl, and such a good-natured look at me. "Well," said he to her, "well, my little dear, leave this black doll with me; and when you come again with your aunt, you shall see what I have done."

The aunt thanked Mr Johnson for his pleasant promise, while she was taking off her turban to depart; and away they went, the Newfoundland dog, Nep., leaping down stairs before them, to show them the way. They were from Buckinghamshire, and had lodgings only a few streets distant. The aunt was Mrs Brown, her niece was Mary Hope. Mary Hope's father was a clerk in the Bank; but she chiefly lived with her aunt in the country, as her father had seven other daughters, and a small salary.

As soon as they were gone, Mr Johnson told his son to tear off all my burnt clothes, scrape me all over with the back of a knife, and then wash me well with soap and water. When this was done, the good-natured artist painted me all over from head to foot. When I was dry he again painted me all over with a warmer colour, like flesh; and when that also was dry, he painted my cheeks, and lips, and eye-brows; and finally he gave me a complete skin of the most delicate varnish. My beautiful hair was entirely burned off; and Mr Johnson said this was a sad pity, as he did not know how to supply it. But his son told him there was a doll's wig-shop very near the Temple, where a new head of hair could be got. So the kind Mr Johnson took the measure of my head; and when he went out for his evening walk, he went to the shop and bought me a most lovely dark auburn wig, with long ringlets, and his son glued it on. When all was done, they hung me up in a safe place to dry.

The hanging up to dry immediately reminded me of my infancy in the shop of Mr Sprat, when I first dangled from the beam and looked round upon all my fellow-creature dolls who were dangling and staring and smiling on all sides. The recollection was, on the whole, pleasing. I seemed to have lived a long time since that day. How much I had to recollect! There was the doll-shop in Holborn—and little Emmy, who used to read little books in the back-room—the Marcet books, the Harriet Myrtle books, the Mary Howitt books, and the delightful story of 'The Good-natured Bear'[1]—in short, all the different stories and histories, and voyages, and travels, and fairy-tales she had read—and there was the master of the shop in his brown paper cock'd hat—and Thomas Plummy and the cake—and Ellen Plummy, and Twelfth-night in the pastry-cook's shop—and the different scenes that I had witnessed among the little milliners; and the making of my first frock and trousers under the tent, upon Ellen Plummy's bed; and my life in Hanover square, during which I saw so many great places in great London, and had been taught by Lady Flora's governess to write, and had fallen headlong from a box at the Opera, into a gentleman's hat; and where, after having beautiful ball-dresses made, my little lady mamma and I had both caught fire; and, lastly, there was my tumble over the wall into the passage, where the Newfoundland dog had fancied I was a broiled bone, and caught me up in his mouth. Here was a biography to recollect; while, for the second time in my life, I was hanging up for my paint and varnish to dry.

CHAPTER XII.

PUNCH AND JUDY.

————◆————

When Mary Hope and her aunt came again to the portrait-painter's house, he presented me to her with a smiling look. "There, Miss Mary," said he, "you see I have been at work upon this child of yours, and I think with good effect. And now that the countenance can be seen, we should observe that *this* doll has really very good features. I mean that they are more marked than is common with dolls. She has a good nose; very bright eyes; and what is very uncommon to see in a doll—she has something like a chin. She has, also, a very pretty mouth, and a sensible forehead. But another remarkable discovery I have made is that of her name! This bracelet which I have cleaned and brightened,

I find to be gold, and upon it is engraved 'MARIA POPPET'!"

Mary Hope received me with great pleasure, and gave Mr Johnson many, many thanks for his kindness in taking so much pains about me. "But what dress," said she, "is this you have given her? is it not too warm?" "I fear it is," said Mr Johnson, laughing. "It is only a bit of green-baize for a wrapper, and an old silver cord for a girdle, which I happened to have at hand, and thought this was better than nothing. You can make her a nice new summer dress when you get home." Mary declared she would do so that very day.

The sitting for Aunt Brown's portrait being concluded, she went down stairs with Mary; who carried me, tossing me up in the air for joy, and catching me as I was falling. This frightened me very much, and I was so glad when we got down stairs. Upon the mat we found the great dog Nep. asleep. He jumped up in a moment, and went bouncing out before us into the street. A hackney coach was waiting at the door, and directly the steps were let down Nep. jumped in first. We arrived at their lodgings, which were very comfortable and very quiet. I much enjoyed the quiet, after all the alarms, and dangers, and narrow escapes, and troubles,

I had recently gone through. The weather was *very* rainy, nearly the whole week, so that I was never taken out during that time; but the days passed very pleasantly, as I often heard Mary read pretty books aloud to her aunt. She also busied herself in making me new clothes, for indeed I wanted everything, as at this time my only dress was the green-baize robe, with the bit of old silver cord round the waist, which Mr Johnson had given me.

One fine day, after the bad weather was over, a hackney coach was at the door waiting to take us out somewhere. Down we went, Neptune, as usual, running down stairs before us with his red tongue out, and leaping in first. "Now Mary," said her aunt, as we drove along, "shall we go to the Exhibition of Pictures at the Royal Academy in Trafalgar square? (Neptune, *do* not poke your great nose so upon my knees—) or shall we go to the Diorama in the Regent's Park? (Neptune, your paws are not clean—you will soil my silk gown—) or shall we go to the Panorama in Leicester square? (Neptune, your nose is *so* cold—) or shall we go to the British Museum?"[14]

"Oh dear aunt," said Mary, "I do not know which is best. I should like to go to them all! (Nep., you must *not* lick the doll's face—the fresh paint may come off!)"

"But you cannot see all in the same day," said her aunt.

"No, aunt," replied Mary, "I know that—only I could not help saying what I should like. Let us go first, then, to the British Museum. But will they let me take Maria Poppet in with me?"

"I should think they would hardly object," said her aunt, "for I never yet saw a doll left among the walking sticks and umbrellas at the door, however plain the doll might be. They could never object to a pretty doll like Maria—though, to be sure, she might be better dressed. Really, you must make haste with her clothes. I cannot let you take her out any more in that strange dress Mr Johnson tied round her."

Mary promised to finish my clothes in a day or two. At this moment the coach stopped, in consequence of a crowd that was assembled in the street round a performance of Punch and Judy.

Mary's aunt put down the glass at one side in order to see what occasioned the stoppage; and as it was quite impossible for the coach to go on immediately, both Mary and her aunt sat looking out of the window at the acting of Mr Punch. He was behaving in his usual naughty and impudent way, and was now pretending to nurse his child. This child was a wooden doll, dressed in an old green sort of night-gown, not unlike the colour of my own green wrapper. Presently the child was heard to cry very loudly; so Mr Punch declared he would have nothing to do with such a cross child, and would throw it out of the window. The child cried again; and Punch actually did what he had threatened, and tossed the wooden doll out upon the heads of the crowd who were gathered around, and it fell somewhere among them. This produced such scrambling and confusion and laughing and noise that it made Neptune jump up in our coach and thrust his head out of the coach window to see what was the matter. When the people saw this they laughed louder than before, and made more noise, so that Nep., thinking they meant to be rude to us, began to bark and throw himself about from one side to the other; in doing which he accidentally ran his head against Mary's shoulder, with such a jerk that he knocked me out of her arms, and I fell down among the crowd!

"Oh, Nep., Nep.," cried Mary, "what *have* you done?"

In a moment out of the window jumped Neptune, and began to scramble through the crowd in search of me, barking away as loud as he could. The disturbance and confusion increased; but who shall describe my dismay when I saw Nep., in his haste, seize upon the child of Mr Punch and carry it back in his mouth to the coach instead of me; while at the same moment a tall man, picking me up, handed me into Punch's show, saying, "Here, take your child, Mr Punch!"

CHAPTER XIII.

THE CITY.

How long it was before the performance concluded I do not know, as I was in so distressed and
confused a state of mind. All I can remember is
that I was thrown headlong into a small box, among
a number of dirty old wooden dolls dressed in rags
and bits of cloth of all colours. Here I lay a few
minutes, till a shrill, squeaking voice, that came
through somebody's nose, cried out "Hurray!" and
then down tumbled Mr Punch himself into the box,
right across me, and the lid of the box was instantly

shut down, and there we all lay squeezed together
in the dark.

I soon began to feel wretchedly uncomfortable—
it was so close and hot, and I also had a very bad
head-ache, owing to something that pressed hard
upon my head. When the box was next opened I
found it was Mr Punch's high-crowned wooden hat
that had hurt me, in consequence of one of its hard
corners pressing against the back of my head.

The master of the show now began to take
some of us out for a morning's performance, and to
arrange the dolls upon a board in the order in which
he should want them to make their appearance.
"Now," said he, "I want the infant" (meaning
Punch's child) "I want the infant—where is Punch's
young one?" Then taking me up—"Ah! what is
this?" said he, "how did this creature come here?
Why, somehow, she has got here in the place of the
infant. She must have popped in by mistake, during
the noise in the street with that great barking dog.
Well, she's too big for me, and she's much too good
to throw away, so I had better sell her."

He had scarcely uttered these words when the
sound of "Clo'! clo'! clo'!"[15] met our ears, and
the master of the show immediately issued from
underneath his curtains, with me in his hand, and

beckoned the Jew clothesman to come to him. He proposed to sell me; and, after half an hour's bargaining, during which so many words were exchanged that my patience was quite worn out, and I did not care what became of me, the Jew carried me away in his bag. I felt myself quite as disagreeably situated as when squeezed among the family of Mr Punch, for my companions in the bag appeared to be two old waistcoats, with hard metal buttons pressing against my left cheek, an old hat, three pairs of old shoes, seven pairs of slippers, a humming top, a teetotum, a snuffer-tray, a coat that seemed greasy, a tin pot, some old gold lace, a bundle of rags, seven bones, two rabbit skins, a stuffed parrot, the head of a rocking horse, a tin box and canister, a cow's horn, a pound of yellow soap, a woollen nightcap, five pairs of worsted stockings, a parcel of tobacco, and half a roast goose. I was sadly afraid that the brass buttons, and the edges of the tin box and canister, the snuffer-tray, or the head of the rocking horse, or the beak of the stuffed parrot, would destroy the beautiful complexion Mr Johnson had given me, when fortunately the very same idea occurred to the cautious mind of the wise old Jew, who suddenly put his hand into the bag, and, thrusting my head and shoulders into a worsted stocking, he rolled

the rest of me tightly in the coat, and then crammed
me into the old hat, with my legs upwards. One
of my hands, however, happened accidentally to be
left free; and, in cramming me into the hat, which
fitted very tight, this hand went through a split in
the edge of the crown. I should not have thought
much of this circumstance, but that I presently
discovered the hat to have a strong scent of otto of
rose, and then I suddenly recollected that this must
be the very hat into which I had fallen at the Opera.
My first acquaintance with the hat having been in the
most fashionable place in London, this was a strange
place of meeting for both of us.

In the evening, when the Jew arrived at his
lodgings, and had eaten his supper of fried soles
and German sausage, with a bunch of white turnip
radishes, he emptied the whole contents of his bag
out on the floor, and bent over us from his chair,
for some minutes, with a face of great satisfaction.
He had collected all this bag-full in one day. "Yes,"
said he, taking me up from all the rest, "yes, this is
the best part of my day's work." I was beginning to
feel pleased at this compliment, when the Jew added,
"this is a beautiful wooden doll, but her gold bracelet
is the thing for me!" So I saw it was not I, but my
gold bracelet that pleased his fancy.

He took me to a little table; and there, with a pair of pincers, he took off my bracelet; and, in its place, he fastened a stupid piece of tin, upon which, with the point of a broken fork, he scratched, "Maria Poppet". I could have cried bitterly at the change, but I was able to restrain myself.

I felt that I should not remain long with the old Jew, because he would soon sell me. The very next day he actually did sell me; and my purchaser was an Italian organ-boy.

This boy had been used to carry a monkey about on the top of his organ,[16] who sat there in a red jacket and soldier's cap, and made faces, while the boy's little sister went round to collect halfpence in a tambourine. This poor little monkey had caught a very bad cold, by being out in the rain one night; and had died; and the Italian boy had come to the Jew, to know if he would buy it to stuff for a glass case. The old Jew considered a long while, and then said he could give no money for the poor little pug, but he would give him something that would be better for him, because it would help him to *make* money. So saying, he offered me to the boy, in exchange for the monkey. The Italian boy hesitated at first; he said he wanted a little money. But his sister exclaiming, "Oh, do, brother, let us have the doll!" he consented; and, fitting on me the red jacket, he stuck me upon the top of the organ, and off we went into the street, to the tune of 'I'd be a butterfly!' which he immediately began to play.

We went through many streets, playing various tunes by the way, and getting many pennies and halfpennies, until we arrived at Guildhall, when Brigitta (that was the little girl's name) said she wanted to run in and show me two very large dolls indeed, called Gog and Magog.[17] "So do," said her brother (whose name was Marco), "and while you go I'll play the tune I think Gog and Magog would like best;" and he immediately began once more to play 'I'd be a butterfly!'

We ran in and saw the great ugly things. Oh, they were such great dolls! and it was such a large room! Out ran Brigitta again, and we went to the Mansion house and played 'Sweet home,'—in the middle of which a fat gentleman, who had just come out of a pastrycook's, put a slice of plum cake into Brigitta's tambourine. We then went and played 'Cherry ripe' in front of the Monument, but we did not play long, as Brigitta got frightened; it looked so high she was afraid it would tumble down and spoil dolly. We next went and played in front of the London tavern, in Bishopsgate street; but there happened to be a great "public dinner" going on, so one of the waiters told us to go away, as there was an alderman just then making a "speech", and we disturbed him; so we walked slowly away, playing 'They're all nodding'.[18]

We now went to St Paul's churchyard and played the 'Old Hundredth Psalm', and 'God save the Queen', and 'Cherry ripe'. I never saw anything before or since that looked so great to me as St Paul's, for although there was a most beautiful doll shop within sight, I could not help looking all the time at the great building.

After this, as we had made one shilling and sevenpence in the course of the day, we went home to Marco's lodgings. He had a little room behind the back kitchen of a cobbler's house in the neighbourhood of London bridge. Brigitta placed me on a straw mattress up in one corner, and then took out two plates and a mug without a handle from a cupboard in the wall, and Marco then laid upon the plate several things to eat, which he had bought on their way home, among which I saw something that looked very much like an ounce of sugar candy, besides the piece of plum cake that had been put into Brigitta's tambourine. They were very merry over their supper. Then Marco, who was very tired from having carried the organ about all day, fell fast asleep, and Brigitta presently took out from a little bundle several pieces of bright scarlet and green stuff, and, in the neatest manner possible, began to make me a very pretty dress, just like the one she had on herself. I was very glad of this, for I did not at all like being dressed like the monkey. She was a very pretty little girl of about nine years of age, with a dark brown complexion and red lips, and large black eyes, and long, black, glossy, curling hair.

I passed several weeks with this merry little mamma, who was always laughing, or chattering, or playing the tambourine and collecting halfpence in it, or dancing me about, except when I sat upon the organ in the place of the monkey. I saw a great deal of London by this means, but more particularly of the City, as far as from Temple Bar to the Thames Tunnel,[19] because Marco knew a great many houses where there were children who liked to hear the organ, and he and his sister generally visited each house about once a week.

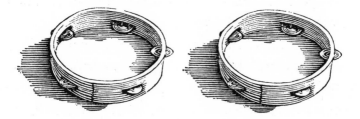

CHAPTER XIV.

THE LORD MAYOR'S SHOW.

———◆———

The day approached for the Lord Mayor's Show. Marco determined that Brigitta should see it; and my pretty Italian mamma determined that I should see it too, so out we went early to get a good place, Marco leaving the organ at home, up in one corner, as he said the Lord Mayor would be sure to have plenty of music without his help, and they should find the organ very troublesome to themselves, and other people too, in a great crowd. We arrived in Cheapside about eight o'clock. On the way we had turned up a little alley, where a man kept an early breakfast stall, and had two pints of hot coffee and two thick slices of bread and butter; and when these were eaten, Marco bought two more, which he wrapped up in a large cabbage-leaf, and put into his pocket. He said they were sure to get hungry with waiting in the street.

Well, as I said, we got into Cheapside before eight o'clock. It was a foggy morning, and wet and muddy underfoot. But still there were a great many people going backwards and forwards, and all looking very busy and anxious. We first chose a spot near Bow church; but very soon a number of tall people came and stood in front of us, so that we could not see through them, nor over their heads. Marco said to one of the tallest of the men, "I wish you would be so kind as to move a little, sir, we cannot see over your head." "Oh," said this unkind man, "suppose you find another place." "And so let us," said Brigitta, "for we can see nothing here through these tall bodies. Come, Marco." We accordingly walked on.

We had only gone a few paces when Marco said he recollected there had been a fire in Cheapside only a few days ago on the opposite side of the way, and as there could not have been time to build a new house, or even pull down the old one, we might perhaps get up into the ruins somewhere. He was quite right. There stood the black shell of the house, with some wooden planks in front of all the lower windows. The crowd was now fast collecting.

We ran across, and pushing aside one of the planks, in we got,—scrambled over a great quantity of rubbish, and black bricks and beams, and smoke and dirt, and broken things,—and with great difficulty Marco climbed up the remains of a broken staircase to see if it could be safely attempted. "Now, Brigitta," said he, when he was up on a broad beam running close underneath the first-floor windows, "Now, Brigitta, it's all safe, come up."

"But how shall I get the poppet up?" said Brigitta.

"Oh," said Marco, "make haste, for I see more people getting in by the windows, and you will lose your place. Throw her up to me! make haste!"

I trembled from head to foot. But before I had time to think more about my fears, the little girl pitched me up in the air, and in the cleverest way possible Marco caught me in his two hands. Then up got Brigitta, and the first thing she did was to station me between two broken bricks at the side of the window, so that I could look down from this height upon the whole of the Lord Mayor's Show as it passed in the street beneath. We had an excellent place at the middle window of the ruined case of the burnt house.

We had not been here a minute before a crowd of people got in through the planks below, several of which were broken down, and in they came rushing, and tried to clamber up to the windows. However, we three kept our good places.

And now came peppering down a shower of rain, and then another shower of rain stronger than the first, and then there came another shower of rain that lasted an hour; and then there was a thick yellow fog for another hour, and then the rain ceased, and the fog began to clear away; and when the fog was gone, suddenly the sun came out, and shone very brightly.

"Now," said Marco, "let us eat our other slices of bread and butter." This they did with great pleasure; the sun shining like gold upon the butter all the time.

They had scarcely done eating when "boom!" came the sound of a great drum,—and all sorts of musical instruments struck up, and the boom of the great drum was quickly followed by the "rub-a-dub row-de-dow" of smaller drums, and the "too-ra-loo" of fifes, and then we saw the show coming along the streets. The streets were lined with soldiers who made a long alley; on the outsides of the soldiers next the houses the crowds were struggling to look over the soldiers' heads; and along the inside of the alley formed by the soldiers, the show came pompously along in the middle of the street.

I have said that I was seated between two broken bricks, at one side of the wall, and next to me was Brigitta. There were at least five people standing behind us at the same window, looking over our heads, and behind Brigitta was a person in a water-proof cape, part of which hanging over Brigitta's left shoulder, came just in front of my face. Brigitta perceived this, and several times pushed the cape back to enable me to see; but as the show came on and got finer and finer, and more thick with men all dressed in colours, and silks, and ribbons, and gold lace,—and the horses in their fine harnesses and trappings came nodding and dancing along, and the coaches got more golden and shining with fat figures in cocked hats sitting inside, and very fat gentlemen with red faces in splendid waistcoats, and the crowds of cocked hats, and multitudes of knees with shining buckles increased,—of all this splendour I had only time to take one look, and then the heavy cape again fell before my eyes, and Brigitta was too much engaged herself to think any more of removing it. However, I did occasionally manage to see, because the person in the water-proof cape moved about, and often bent himself from side to side to see

better, and once when he did so I got sight of the
two men in armour,—two men covered all over,
—one in iron and one in brass, just as lobsters
are covered with their shells, only shining in the
sun, and riding on large black horses.   Besides
these I also saw the principal dolls of this wonderful
show—I mean the Lord Mayor in his coach, with
the wooden Sword-bearer and the gingerbread
Mace-bearer—at least, they looked like wood and
gingerbread; and, indeed, so did the Lord Mayor
himself. The Sword-bearer and the Mace-bearer both
sat back to back at the open windows in a thorough
draught, and they both appeared to have got colds in
their noses. We had an excellent view of the Lord
Mayor in his robe of scarlet, with gold and coloured
stripes over it, and wearing a beautiful necklace hanging down upon his breast. He gave a sigh as he passed
us, and laid his hand upon his fine stomach, and then
he gave a smile. The coach was drawn by eight horses
with proud necks, all covered with rich aprons, and
ribbons, and straps, and tassels, and tinkerums and
things, and with quantities of coloured ribbon-bows,
and streamers and gold lace, and brass nails and
buckles.   Then the coach—oh, what a coach!   It
was like a coach made of glass set in a very fine,
fancy looking-glass frame, and stuck on a sort of

gilded car all covered with paintings and golden carvings and sweetmeats, extremely like several coaches I had seen on twelfth-cakes, only a great deal bigger. I wondered very much if it was made of sugar.

We waited till the procession returned; it was a long time, but we were determined to wait. When they all came back we saw, besides the fine gentlemen, a number of beautiful fat ladies in feathers, with diamonds and rosy cheeks, the fattest of whom, and the most beautiful of course, was the Lady Mayoress in an apricot satin dress with all sorts of embroidery, and lace, and ribbons, and spangles, and precious things, and looking all so stiff and expensive behind the glass, but yet seeming to be alive, although afraid to move in the least for fear of injuring some part of all this dress. I thought it was so kind of everybody in the show to take the time and trouble to let themselves be dressed for us to see them.

All of a sudden we heard a great crack, and then a loud cry from a number of people below, "The wall is falling! come down, all of you!" No one wanted a second warning, and all who were up at the windows went scrambling down as quick as they could, and in the best way they could; but how it was all done I have no notion, as Marco had suddenly seized me, and thrust me, head foremost, into his pocket, where I remained for two or three hours, and when next taken out I found myself in the little back room, where they were going to have some supper of macaroni.

CHAPTER XV.

THE LOST BRACELET.

———◆———

The next events of my life were two pleasures and one pain. The pain was a change of circumstances, and the first pleasure was the possession of a new wardrobe. How could I have a new wardrobe, when my mamma was only the little sister of a poor Italian organ-boy, and had but one dress for herself? It all came about through what I considered, at the time, a great misfortune; it was the change of my present mamma for another; and I was very fond of my little Italian mamma, and therefore was sorry to be obliged to leave her.

The day after Lord Mayor's day was cold and wet; but, notwithstanding, we all went out with the organ, for Marco said we must earn some money

to make up for yesterday, which was a day of pleasure; so we went round to several houses where he
was accustomed to play. At last we got into Finsbury square, and there began to play before a house
where a little girl called Lydia Thomson lived.
Her papa was a partner in the house of Barclay and
Perkins,[20] the great brewers, and she used to come
out on the balcony when Marco played, and always
threw him a penny, and sometimes danced up and
down the balcony to his music. Well, while we were
playing on this cold wet day, it began to snow, and
little Lydia, who was dancing on the balcony, was
obliged to run into the warm drawing-room for fear
she should catch cold; and when she looked out,
she thought Brigitta seemed so wet and cold in the
snow, that she almost began to cry, and asked her
mamma to let us all come in. Her mamma gave
us leave, so down she ran and brought us all in, and
placed us by a warm parlour fire. Then away she
ran to her mamma again, and presently came back
dancing and skipping about before a servant, who
carried a tray with two plates full of roast mutton
and potatoes from the servants' dinner, and she told
Marco and Brigitta to begin to eat, and they laughed
and looked so pleased, and ate away, and began to
look so much warmer and more comfortable. Then

away she ran again, and brought down a box full
of sweetmeats and sugar-plums, and put it down
before Brigitta, and said, "That is for you," and
Brigitta kissed her hand to her so prettily, and said,
"Thank you, dear little lady." Then Marco asked
if he might play to her, and she said, "Oh yes," so
he played all his tunes, and she danced up and down
the passage, and in and out of the room.

When all the tunes were done, Marco said, "Now
we must go," so they bid good bye, and the servant
opened the door, and the wind blew in very cold.
So the little girl said, "Shut the door again, and
wait a minute," and ran away again to her mamma;
and after about five minutes, down she came, bringing a warm woollen shawl for Brigitta, and an old
cape of her papa's for Marco, and she said, "My
mamma gives you these." Oh, they were so much
obliged to her. They thought her such a dear,
kind little girl; and Brigitta's large black eyes filled
with tears while she thanked her, but little Lydia
only danced and jumped about.

Then Brigitta put on the shawl, and took me up,
and I thought she was going to carry me away
with her, but she said, "Dear, kind little lady,
take this doll from me; it is such a great pleasure
to me to have something to give you." Lydia

said, "But you like to have the doll." "No, no!" answered Brigitta, "take it, dear little lady!" So she and Marco hurried away, and left me with Lydia Thomson.

I was at first very sorry to be parted from my merry Italian mamma; but I soon became very fond of this kind little Lydia. She used to play with me a great deal, and she took off that ugly tin bracelet from my arm, but not till she had read my name—"Maria Poppet". She dressed me very nicely, too, so that I had, as I have said, a new wardrobe; and a very few days after I was settled in this new home, I had the second pleasure I have mentioned. It happened in this manner.

One very cloudy morning, a voice crying "Clo'! clo'!" came down Finsbury square, and stopped in front of our house. Again the voice said, "Clo'!" and then, after stopping a little, said very quickly, "Clo'! clo'!" I recollected whose voice that was in a moment, and it made me tremble. It was the old Jew who had bought me of Punch's showman.

Lydia had left me sitting at the nursery window, with my nose and cheek resting against the glass; I could therefore look out, and I now saw him walk up to the area, and poke his head through the iron rails, looking down, so that I only saw his round shoulders and his rusty black bag. Now I heard the area door open, as if one of the maids was coming out, and instantly the Jew said, "My dear, I want to speak something!" "Speak then," said the merry voice of my mamma's nursery maid.

"Come up the area steps, my dear," said the Jew; "it's a cold wind, and I'm rather hoarse to-day; and besides, my dear, I've something of great consequence to speak."

The nursery maid ran up, saying, "Well, be quick then."

"Yes, my dear," said the Jew, and then, lowering his voice, he said, "You've got a wooden doll in this house, my dear." I trembled more than ever at this; I thought he had come for me.

"Well," said the nursery maid, "and what of that?—is that all you've got to say, with your whispering and winking, and screwing your face?"

"Not all, my dear," said the Jew. "Your doll is a doll of some rank and consequence, and her family name is Poppet, and her other name is Maria."

"Well, lauk now!" said the maid, "how did you guess that?"

"Guess it, my dear," said the Jew, "I knew it long ago. She used to have a bracelet upon her arm, with the name engraved upon it."

"Yes, so she had, so she had," said the maid; "a tin one it was."

The Jew laughed, and said, "A gold one, my dear. It was tin when you had her, I dare say; but formerly, in the days of her greatness, my dear, she had one made of pure gold, and I can tell you what"—here he again lowered his voice—"I know where the gold one is. I can find it. Yes, my dear, I can, and I may as well just let you have a peep at it." Here the Jew drew something in a paper out of his pocket, and held it up.

"Oh my!" said the nursery maid, "well, if ever! There's Maria Poppet engraved upon it—and you've brought it back to young missis. Oh, how pleased she will be!"

"Yes, my dear," said the Jew, putting it back into his pocket. "You can tell them what you've seen, and say that I have no objection to sell it, to oblige them—and it's pure gold, you know, my dear, and I'll come again to-morrow morning. Clo'! clo'! clo'!" and away he went, leaving the poor nursery maid calling out after him in vain.

Well, this was the talk of the whole house. Everybody was so much interested about it. Next morning the Jew came, and asked to see Mrs Thomson. He was shown into the passage, and then he produced the gold bracelet, which fitted my wrist exactly, and everybody admired it very much, particularly Lydia, who kissed it several times.

"You will sell it, of course?" said Mrs Thomson.

After long hesitation and consideration, the Jew named his price. Mrs Thomson then made him an offer of some money for it, but the Jew said he could melt it, and make more by it than that.

At the sound of "melting" it, Lydia began to cry bitterly, so we were all sent away into the nursery, and told to wait till Mrs Thomson came to us. How it was settled I do not know, but after waiting about half an hour, we heard the sound of "Clo'! clo'!" and Mrs Thomson came up stairs, bringing the bracelet in her hand, and that very day it was fastened on my wrist, as at first.

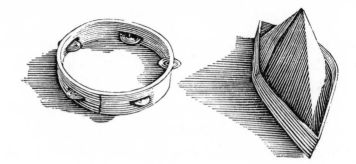

CHAPTER XVI.

THE NEW GRAND CHRISTMAS PANTOMIME.

———◆———

Lydia Thomson had long been promised to be taken to the next Christmas Pantomime, and the happy day for this was now arrived. All the morning long, Lydia was so restless, she was unable to remain quiet for two minutes together. If she sat down to work, she was often obliged to get up and dance, and then to run and look out at the window,—then to run down stairs singing,—then to hop up again upon one leg,—then to run and look at the play-bill, and read it all through aloud,—then to try and read it topsy-turvy, and ask me to help her,—then to dance me up in the air,—then to run and roll over and over with me on the sofa, crying out, "Oh, Maria! oh, Maria! we're going to see the New Grand Christmas Pantomime!"

At last the evening came. We were dressed in good time. My mamma, Lydia, wore a white frock and blue sash, and looked very nice; but she made me look beautiful, for she said I should be dressed in a way to suit a beautiful pantomime; so she made me a frock of thin white muslin, and trimmed it with some little pink roses that her mamma gave her, and put a wreath of little pink roses round my hair. The carriage came to the door, and we drove off to Drury-lane Theatre.[21] There were Lydia's papa and mamma, and her two cousins, and out they all jumped, ran past the crowd at the door, and up the stairs, till we reached a private box, which was exactly over one side of the stage, upon which we looked down with great expectation. I thought we should have seen better if we had been in a box in the middle of the theatre, but still this was very nice. We did nothing but clap our hands and look at the dark curtain. The play was over. We had not been allowed to come till the play was over, because Lydia's papa said he knew we should be tired if we did.

The house was very full of people, and I began to look round me, and up and down in all directions. But who shall describe my pleasure and surprise when, looking up into the two-shilling gallery, who should I see sitting in the very front row but the celebrated Mr Sprat! On one side of him was his wife, who appeared to be eating periwinkles; on the other side sat his two sons and daughter; so that they every one of them had a front seat. Looking down into the pit, who should I next see but the master of the doll shop, who had fancied himself Napoleon in a brown paper cocked hat, with his daughter and little Emmy at his side: but what gave me far greater pleasure was to see very near them, though a little in front, Ellen Plummy and her brother Thomas. Oh, my dear little Ellen Plummy, how I wished you were up here with us! She sat on the right-hand side of Thomas, and on his left was Nanny Bell. I now looked again round the house, and in a private box nearly opposite to ours, but larger and lower down, I saw a pretty, delicate little girl, most elegantly dressed, whom I at once recognized as my little lady mamma, Flora. I was so glad to be unable to see the least sign of any scars from the fire. She was in the middle of this large box, leaning over. At one side, almost hidden behind a red curtain and her large silk cloak, sat Lady Flowerdale. Somehow I immediately thought of Mary Hope, to whom I had been taken by the dog Nep. I did not see her, it is true; but while I was thinking of her, and looking down into the pit, I saw Mr Johnson, the portrait painter, peeling an orange. Looking at Mr Johnson, with gratitude for all he had done for me after my burning, it naturally made me think of how much more gratitude I owed to the celebrated Mr Sprat, who had made me, and I immediately looked up again towards the gallery where he sat. But happening at first to look too high, I caught sight, in the one-shilling gallery, of my little Italian mamma, Brigitta, and her brother Marco. They were laughing, talking, and cracking nuts.

Now we began to long for the Pantomime to begin. Presently we heard all manner of sounds going on behind the curtain—all manner of voices talking and calling, and buzzing and humming. The moving of boards, and hammering, and the placing of planks and beams, and pushing and pulling about of heavy things; and now and then through one side of the curtain we caught a glimpse of something so bright that went by, like tall flags on painted poles, and tops of spears, and parts of mantles of people's dresses; and once, underneath the bottom of the dark green curtain, we saw run along a little pair of bright silver feet. The sound of drums and trumpets was also heard to begin in a disorderly manner, and then stop suddenly, and end

in a murmur of many voices, and a hurrying to and
fro of many feet.

And now the band of musicians that played in
the long orchestra beneath us, came thronging in,
and seized upon all sorts of very great and very
small instruments, and began blowing and twanging,
and trying up and down, and backwards and forwards, and squeaking high and flourishing about,
and rumbling and tumbling, and working very hard
to get into order.   Then they were quite silent.
Then *tap! tap!* went the fiddlestick of the leader of
the orchestra, who sat upon his high stool—there
was more silence than ever—and suddenly off they
all went, all the instruments at once, and played
away in a most wonderful manner—slow music, and
quick music, and grand marches, and all sorts of
dances, that made everybody's heart jump within
and try to do whatever the music was doing.

The band ceased playing, and very slowly indeed
the dark curtain began to be drawn up. As it went
creeping up towards the high roof, we gradually saw
a great field in winter, all white with snow, and the
snow coming down. As the dark curtain went up
and the snow came down, it seemed that the box we
were in was sinking downwards also. However, it
did not.

The scene we looked upon was a very large field of snow, with shrubs in the front all covered with snow, and large trees at the side all covered with snow, and great woods at the back. The snow presently ceased to fall, and we saw ranges of hills behind the woods quite white like the rest. All the time the music continued to play something that was so slow, and cold, and soft, and melodious, and grand.

The music was changed to an ugly, broken, hobbling, harsh sound, and at the farthest end of the field we saw a strong-made, little old man, in a dark blue cloak, appear, and come down towards the white shrubs in front, just under us. His hat was the shape of an extinguisher, but with a broad brim. As he approached, we saw that he had a large blue nose, and very large uneven teeth, and blue goggle eyes! Ugh! how we all shivered, except Lydia's papa and mamma, who laughed and told us not to be frightened. The music stopped, and this ugly, strong Dwarf then repeated these words:—

"The frosty air shall take them,
And the wintry wind shall shake them,
And frozen boughs shall rake them,
While rocks and ruins break them,—
And years shall always snip them,
While hours for ever trip them

And constant trouble dip them,
Until Time come and clip them;
All this shall be done to destroy all their dances,
And drive from the world its delightful romances."

As the ugly, thick-limbed little Dwarf said this,
he stamped one foot,—a loud wind was heard, and
in a moment he went straight down through the
earth, and was quite gone! At the same moment
we heard a sweet voice singing in the air, which
said—

"He thinks he makes what mortals see:
It seems so—but it shall not be."

Before we had time to recover ourselves, we saw
that the whole scene of frost and snow was changing
into a bright summer. The green leaves came out
upon the trees—the sun-beams shot across the sky,
and played upon the distant woods and hills—a
warm, glowing colour came all over the scene—and
while the music played the prettiest dance, we saw
the spire of a village church slowly rise up among
the trees at the back, and a troop of villagers, with
wreaths and garlands of flowers, all came dancing
in, and round and round.

And now came in a very pretty little village girl
with her lover; and the dancers all surrounded them

with their garlands, and they were all going to be very happy, when a cross-looking old man in an earth-coloured flannel gown, who was the father of the pretty little village girl, hobbled in and separated them,—and would not allow it,—and made signs that the young man was not rich enough to have his daughter. He made signs that the young man had no fields, and orchards, and dogs, and horses, and houses, and money, and these were the things that he thought most to be loved, and therefore that they made the best lover. So the young man having none of these, was driven away by the old father and two of his men with pitchforks. When, just as they were driving him out, a noise was heard as if a great many penny trumpets were blown. All the villagers made signs of seeing something wonderful coming. Then came the sound of one single penny trumpet, and immediately afterwards there entered, with a very consequential strut, a figure with a large round head and red cheeks, scarcely any body, and very thin grass-green legs, and carrying in both hands an immense brass trumpet, which, however, had only the sound of a very small penny one.

"I come," said he, "to herald the advance of the King of Bubble Island,—and I am his chief trumpeter." Upon which he lifted up his immense brass trumpet, which said, *"Twee, te-twee, twee!"*

Now came in twenty more trumpeters like the first, all with large trumpets, blowing *"Twee! twee! twee!"* After them came marching in an army, all the soldiers having helmets made of great white turnips, with the green leaves nodding about for feathers, and carrying shields of black glass, in the middle of each of which was seen a bowl of white soap-suds and a pipe. These were followed by the King's Prime Minister and the other Wise Men of his court, all of them blowing bubbles, which rose into the air and looked most beautiful; and as fast as they burst, the Wise Men blew more, so that there were always a good many floating in the air. Each was attended by two valiant knights in glass armour of bottle green, the one on the right bearing a bowl of soap-suds, and the one on the left carrying a supply of soap and fresh pipes. After these came dancing a great many golden Coins of the Realm, all with the same face, and all of them with thin spider's legs, and their hands in their pockets.

And now came the King himself! He had a large round head of glass, coloured with green and pink, and his face was coloured with green and pink, and he wore a golden crown, with spikes like a dog's collar, which spouted up a great quantity of froth in the shape of feathers. His body was quite round, like his head, only very much larger. His hair was dark purple. He had a short mantle edged with fur like froth, and his legs were the colour of a blue-bottle fly spotted with gold. His walk and air were like all the pride of the earth put into one chemist's bottle! An immense blast of farthing trumpets announced his actual presence!

"Poor people!" exclaimed he, "villagers and people, and things!—ye have dared to harbour among you no less a gentleman than the Prince my son, the heir of all these Bubbles, who has caused us all these troubles,—but what my grief doubles, let me say, is the fact that he has run away, and our Royal Court doth mock——bless my soul! what young man is that in the brown frock?"

The moment he said this, the poor lover, who was just being driven out by the three pitchforks, began to run about and try to hide himself. The Prime Minister and the Wise Men instantly drew from their sides each a telescope, which they drew out to its full length, and began to point in all directions to examine the young man, crying out, "We think it is—we think it is—we think it is the Prince!" The Prime Minister now jumped pick-a-back upon the back of the King's Physician, and pointed the telescope towards the feet of the young peasant, crying out, "Now I shall have him!" When the Physician, on whose back he was, heard this, he began to prance very much. The Prime Minister, whose observations through the telescope were much disturbed by this prancing, then jumped down and lay flat upon his stomach, pointing his glass towards the young man's face, and then called out, "I've got him. It *is* the Prince!" The moment the King heard his Prime Minister declare it to be actually his dear long-lost son, he rushed, as if mad with paternal feelings, towards the young man, and being unable to stop himself in time, he and the Prince together knocked down a cottage! It fell flat down, and they rolled amidst the ruins! The village girls extricated the Prince by the shoulders, and the Wise Men pulled out the King by the legs, drawing him along a good way on the ground, to be sure that he *was* extricated. Then the King immediately remembered how very angry he had been with his son for running away, and was going to knock him down with his golden sceptre, when the father of the pretty little village girl, that the Prince was in love with, ran up and received the blow instead, which knocked him down upon his knees; but instead of getting up, he declared it was the greatest honour of his life to have been knocked down by the father of his daughter's lover, whom he now discovered to be such a great person, and to have so many fields, and bags of gold, and horses, and people, and soap-bubbles.

"Base clodpole!" said his Majesty, "is the Prince my son in love with your little hedge-flower of a daughter?"

Before he could say another word, the Prince himself ran up to the little peasant girl with open arms, crying out—"Yes, King of Bubbles, it is true."

"Then," said the King,—"Blow me!"

At the sound of these words, the most terrible that could be heard in the whole kingdom of Bubble Island, all the army uttered a howl, and the Prime Minister and other Wise Men rushed to their bowls of soap-suds, and filling the air with bubbles to try if their pipes were in the highest degree of perfection, they then advanced towards the King and applied their pipes to different parts of his body to blow him as he ordered. But suddenly was heard a great sound of wind and rain, and the sky got dark, and it began to snow; and while they were all staring at the fast-falling snow, the ugly, strong limbed Dwarf, with the blue nose and goggle eyes, came walking down among them and said—

"I will befriend thee, King of Bubbles,
And all thy foes I'll fill with troubles:

> Come frost and snow! and cover all we see,
> And change the face of life's reality!"

At these words there began to descend a number of dark, heavy clouds, at the same time that a mist rose up from the earth, till the clouds and the mist met, and out of the middle came a great troop of the Spirits of the Frost and Snow, all glistening in white snow and icicles, with branches covered with snow and icicles in their hands, and they all sang this chorus:—

> "We will the face of Nature change,
> And make its pleasant places strange,
> Covering all life with icy wing,
> As thou may'st order, Bubble King."

"Very good," said the King. "I'm much obliged to you, Mr Blue-nosed Dwarf, and to all you ladies and gentlemen with frosty countenances. Now then, at once, I will thank you to cover the village, where all these people live, with snow; to turn that peasant girl, whom my son is so mad and stupid as to be in love with, into a large icicle, and make the Prince a man of snow looking at her."

The Spirits of the Frost instantly seized upon the Prince and the little peasant girl, when suddenly a rosy light appeared in the middle of the dark clouds,

which got brighter and brighter, and sent out rays of
an orange colour, and then rays also of bright purple.
Then the orange began to get golden, and the purple
to turn to bright violet; and then in the middle of
all there opened out a brilliant light, and we saw a
wheel of golden fire slowly turning round, and in
the centre of it stood a little child, who seemed to
be dressed in bright silver gossamer, with beautiful
auburn hair, and a silver wand in her hand, and a
bright violet star upon her forehead; and the little
voice called out,—

> "Spirits of the Frost! I charge ye sing again
> More truly,—mixing pleasure with the pain."

Then the Spirits of the Frost sang these words,—

> "We will the face of Nature change,
> And make the truest things look strange;
> But Nature's heart will ever be
> Deep beyond Fate's tyranny,
> And from King Bubble's surface free."

Then said the Dwarf,—

> "But change is mine, and strife and war,—"

Then replied the Child,—

> "Take them—but work within my law."

The clouds now closed in front of the bright
Child-spirit to the sound of soft music, till each cloud
became of a dull leaden colour as before. Presently
came a loud sound of instruments from behind the
clouds, and a large silver arrow was seen to fly straight
towards the young Prince. It struck him, and he
instantly turned into Harlequin, in a dress of bright
gold and silver and red and blue, and a black mask!
Again the sound of a clang of instruments was heard
behind the clouds, and out dropped a bag of money
upon the head of the village girl's father, which
knocked him down, and when he got up he was
poor old Pantaloon, with a goat's beard, and a pig-
tail, and a short red mantle, and a stick. Again a
clang of instruments was heard, and a great heavy
stone was seen to fly out of the cloud straight at
the glass head of his Majesty, the King of Bubble
Island, which it struck, and,—with a sound like the
breaking of six dozen of soda-water bottles,—his
head flew into a million of pieces, and up in its place
rose the head of the Clown, with his mouth wide
open!—at the same time all the Royal robes of the
King flew up into the air, where they were blown
about in all directions, till they were at last blown
quite away, and there was the Clown, in his ridiculous
red and white patch-work dress! Once more was

heard the clang of instruments behind the clouds, and out of the clouds flew a beautiful bouquet of flowers, which fell upon the head of the little peasant girl, who instantly turned into the prettiest Columbine that ever was seen in all the world. She was like the brightest silver-footed fairy, and yet at the same time she was such a little dear sweetheart.

But what *do* you think happened at this moment? Nobody would ever guess. It was this. My mamma Lydia was in such excessive delight that she sank back with her arms thrown up, and totally forgetting me, I slipped over the edge of the box and fell upon the stage, close to the little silver feet of Columbine. My mamma did not know I had fallen. Columbine had no idea where I came from; so the next time she passed the spot where I lay, she caught me up and ran with me to her room behind the scenes.

CHAPTER XVII.

CONCLUSION.

———◆———

The moment Columbine entered her room she held me up to a good-natured old lady, who was dressing herself like a scaly green dragon for the last scene, and cried out, "Here's a pretty doll I have just found on the stage!"

"Where *did* you get it?" said the good-natured old lady, going to a looking-glass to fit on the dragon's head.

"Oh, grandmother," said Columbine, "I've no time to tell you now, as I have to dance a hornpipe in the next scene. Take care of her." Saying which, away ran the pretty Columbine.

As soon as the old lady had tied the strings of the dragon's head under her chin, so that her face could look through the large red throat and open mouth of the dragon, she held her head on one side before the glass and said, "There! I think that does very nicely." She then folded me up in a handkerchief, and placed me with their bonnets and shawls.

Here I lay, hearing all sorts of noises of trumpets and drums, and singing and dancing, and tumbling about, and calling out, and laughing, and fireworks, and the great rolling of many wheels, and loud sounds of distant applause from the audience. When all was over I was taken home by the Columbine and her grandmother. It was a wet night, and they walked through the rain in shawls and clogs, and holding up a great umbrella with three slits in the top. They lived in the back parlour of a small greengrocer's, near Covent garden. The bed and the rest of the furniture were very humble, the hangings of the bed being of grey draft-board pattern, and the coverlid of the bed of patchwork; but all looking as clean as it was poor.

I now saw that the pleasant old grandmother, who had acted the green dragon, was dressed all in brown, even with a brown bonnet and brown stockings; the umbrella was brown too. Columbine was dressed in a high frock of grey checked gingham, but very neatly made, and she wore a small straw cottage bonnet. Under one arm, however, she had a bundle from which shining things peeped out, and she took a pair of silver slippers out of her pocket, folded them up in a bit of newspaper, and placed them in a little band-box, into which I peeped and saw it was full of precious things. Then down they sat to a supper of boiled eggs, followed by bread and cheese and porter, and endive and beet-root, and then they laughed and talked about the pantomime, and looked at me and examined my gold bracelet; and then went to bed.

I was placed away very carefully the next morning, as the pretty little Columbine had too much to do to attend to me. I was therefore, during all the time of the pantomime, left quite alone. I, however, employed my time by thinking very much over my past life, and going over everything in my own mind, from the day of my birth in the room of the celebrated Mr Sprat, down to the present time.

When the Christmas pantomime was over in London, the little Columbine and her grandmother went into the country, to act at a small theatre there, and they took me with them. After the performances had gone on for three weeks Columbine had a benefit night. The first piece was the tragedy of "Douglas,"[22] and, as no green dragon was wanted in it, the grandmother acted Lady Randolph. The little Columbine acted Norval, with his bow and quiver; she had taken the part, I suppose, on account of its resemblance to Cupid.

Near the town in which the theatre was, there stood a large country mansion, called Ashbourn Hall, and the lady of this mansion was very kind, and took so many tickets for Columbine's benefit that her party filled all the three front boxes.

The next morning the pretty little Columbine took me out of the drawer in which I was lying in the dark, and feeling very dull. I saw that she looked smiling and happy, and was nicely dressed in a neatly made blue frock with white sprigs on it, and a new bonnet. "Come with me, Maria Poppet," said she, "and we shall see if we cannot give them a little pleasure in return for all their kindness;"— so she wrapped me up in silver paper, all but my head. I was still dressed in my pretty muslin frock with pink roses. Away she walked, with me in her hand, to Ashbourn Hall.

First we came up to the high iron gates, and inside I could see a very smooth green lawn, with fine spreading trees about it, and broad gravel

walks, and great round evergreens, and numbers
of gay flowers, and a round fish pond with a fountain
in the middle, and beautiful water lilies growing
in it. Columbine rang the bell, and a good-natured
looking, fat old man-servant opened the gate, and
smiled when he saw her, as if he remembered her.
She said she wished to see Mrs Ashbourn, and he
asked her to walk in. We went up the gravel walk,
and there was a flight of very white stone steps up to
the door, with large flower pots on them; and when we
got in there was a square lobby with a billiard table,
and large pictures on the walls; and then the servant
threw open a door and showed us into the drawing-
room. Oh, it was such a beautiful room! There was a
large bright sparkling fire, and a large bay window
opposite, with a most lovely view out of it, and
flowers-stands full of geraniums and other flowers in
it, and bright crimson curtains, and a bright carpet,
and numbers of sofas and arm-chairs, and ottomans,
and tables with crimson cloths on them, with large
china jars of flowers, and Christmas annuals, and
doll's books, and scent bottles, and all manner of
pretty things; and bookcases, and a piano, and
harp, and guitar, and there was such a sweet scent
in the room; and there was a German piping bullfinch,
who was singing a sweet waltz, and a large white

dog lying asleep on the rug, who, when we came in, raised his head. But what I liked best of all was the sight of a pretty, gentle-looking little girl, about seven years old, who sat on a sofa reading to a handsome, kind-looking lady.

The lady, who was Mrs Ashbourn, rose up and received the little Columbine very kindly, and the little girl came forward and smiled, and held out her hand to her, and they made her sit down by them. Then little Columbine said in the prettiest manner, "I am come, ma'am, to thank you for your kindness to me, and to ask you to allow this young lady to accept of a doll from me."

Mrs Ashbourn thanked her, and said her little girl would be delighted to have such a pretty doll; and so I was placed in the soft little hands of my present dear mamma, Lucy Ashbourn; and then, after a few minutes more talking, in which a great many flattering things were said of me, pretty little Columbine took leave, and left me in the house where I now am.

Here I feel that I am settled for life. Only yesterday, my mamma, as she was sitting on her papa's knee, told him that when she grew too old to play with me, she would give me to her little sister. She takes the greatest care of me. Everything is made for me just like hers. I have morning dresses, afternoon dresses, and night-clothes, and a little chest of drawers to keep my things in. I have a little bed, with white curtains and nice blankets and sheets, in which my mamma lays me every night, after undressing me and putting on my nightgown and nightcap; and in the morning she makes believe to wash me all over, and brushes my hair, and dresses me. When I go out I have a bonnet and cloak put on, and I am always dressed for dinner, and have my hair done. I have also had the happiness to become acquainted with another doll, who lives in a country-house near ours. At different times, when we have been sitting in the garden while our mammas played about, she has told me the history of her life, and I hope at a future time that these 'Memoirs of a Country Doll' will be made public, as mine have been.

I now take an affectionate leave of my readers, who may perhaps hear of me again, when the Country Doll relates her history.

NOTES

1. *There was the lovely book called 'Birds and Flowers', by Mary Howitt; the nice stories about 'Willie', by Mrs Marcet; the delightful little books of Mrs Harriet Myrtle, ... and besides other books, there was oh! such a story-book called 'The Good-Natured Bear'!* (page 9; see also page 73)

The books the doll listened to were all published at about the same time as her *Memoirs*. Mary Howitt's *Birds and Flowers and Other Country Things* demonstrates her typical mixture of information and domestic play. Mrs Marcet was notable among those who wrote information books for children, for she used the formula of the question and answer unusually well and with a real feeling for young behaviour. *Willy's Stories for Young Children* and *Willy's Grammar, interspersed with stories for the use of Children* were both published in 1845. Horne probably also knew the earlier *Willy's Holidays, or Conversations on different kinds of Governments*, which first appeared in 1836. Mrs Marcet was an alert student of her market: *Willy's Travels on the Railroad*, published in 1847, must be one of the earliest books for children about this newfangled form of transport.

I have said something in my introduction about the circumstances of the Harriet Myrtle books, attractive little volumes containing three or four domestic tales, and sometimes a story in verse. A group of letters written by Horne to his publisher, Joseph Cundall, between 1844 and 1847 (now in the Henry Huntington Library) makes it clear that the *Stories of the Seasons* (*Spring; Summer; Little Amy's Birthday*, for autumn; and *The Man of Snow*, for winter) were the work of these two friends, and other books containing the same characters, such as *Pleasures of the Country* and *Home and its Pleasures*, may be added to the list. However, all these books and others by "Harriet Myrtle" have been widely attributed to Lydia Falconer Miller, wife of the geologist, Hugh Miller; and the *Cambridge Bibliography of English Literature* (followed by the British Museum Catalogue) gives to Mary Gillies only *More fun for our little friends* (1864). Standard reference books such as the *Dictionary of National Biography*, Cushing's *Initials and Pseudonyms* and Halkett and Laing's *Dictionary of Pseudonyms*, all assume that there were two ladies, writing at exactly the same date, who both adopted this distinctive pen-name. I find this hard to believe, and the confusion in Cushing by which one Harriet Myrtle is referred to as "Mrs Mary (Gillies) Miller", the other as "Mrs Lydia Falconer Miller", suggests that it will be worth while to follow this study with further investigation of these two authors. Meanwhile, it is obvious that Horne is enjoying the pleasurable irony of referring to his own work in the Myrtle books and in *The Good-Natured Bear*.

2. *One afternoon Emmy had been reading . . . whose name was Napoleon Bonaparte.* (page 10)
  There is more point here if we remember that Horne, with the help of Mary Gillies, had written a *History of Napoleon* (1841). When we add *Napoleon's Remains*, a poem in the *Monthly Magazine*, also in 1841 and an article, *Historical Glance at the Career and Character of Napoleon* in the same magazine in the next year, we can see, perhaps, another case of the anonymous author hinting in the story at his identity.

3. *Twelfth-cake.* (page 11 et seq.)
  Horne's story belongs to a time when the old festivities

of Twelfth Night were running alongside the Pelz-Nickel games and the decked Christmas tree imported from Germany. The elaborate decoration on Twelfth-cakes, such as entranced Maria Poppet, is often mentioned in the Victorian period; and one architectural article compares the house at Kenwood to a Twelfth-cake, since it is "patched all over with panels of filigree work".

4. *"in Bishopsgate Street, near the Flower Pot"*. (page 12)
Horne would know the place especially because an omnibus which started from the Flower Pot ran to Lower Clapton and past the house where the Howitts were living at this time. Mary Howitt writes to Miss Meteyard to ask for "Behind the Pond", as conductors were always changing, and the name *The Elms* "never took".

5. *"His name is 'Achilles'* . . . *fields of Waterloo"*. (page 41)
The Achilles statue, which stands on the edge of the park at Hyde Park Corner, was made in 1822 from cannon taken at the victories of Salamanca, Vittoria, Toulouse and Waterloo.

6. *Queen's Concert Rooms, Hanover Square.* (page 42)
The Hanover Rooms were built in 1775 in the north-west corner of Hanover Square, and were used for musical occasions for nearly a century. Haydn conducted his symphonies there, and between 1833 and 1866 they were the performing centre of the Philharmonic Society. In 1874 the rooms were altered and used for The Circle of Nations, afterwards the Hanover Square Club. The building was demolished in 1900.

7. *a toy-shop in Oxford Street* (page 43)
This was most probably the Pantheon, No. 173, at the

east end of Oxford Street (where Marks and Spencer's Pantheon store now stands). One of the best known places to buy dolls and toys, and often mentioned in children's stories, this porticoed building began in 1772 as "a winter Ranelagh" and thereafter had a varied history as an assembly room, a concert hall and a theatre. In 1834 it was re-opened as a bazaar and continued very popular till 1867, when it was bought by Gilbey, the wine merchants.

8. *the Duke of York's column.* (page 44)

This statue in Carlton House Terrace was relatively new when Horne wrote his story, and it would still be remembered that this tribute to the Grand Old Duke of York cost all ranks of the army a day's pay. The spike projecting from the head of the statue was said to be for filing the Duke's unpaid pills. Up to the late 1880's visitors could walk up the 124 foot column by a staircase.

9. *the Soho Bazaar.* (page 44)

Already an old institution when Horne wrote, this treasure-cave for the young was described by Thomas Allen in *The History and Antiquities of London*, Volume IV (1828) page 309:

"This square has risen into considerable notice, by a very extensive, novel, and curious establishment, founded by John Trotter, esq., a gentleman of considerable opulence and respectability, residing in this place. This institution is denominated a 'bazaar', a well known oriental term for a kind of fixed fair or market.

The premises . . . are very commodious and spacious, containing a space of nearly 300 feet by 130, from the square to Dean-street on one hand and to Oxford-street on the other, consisting of several rooms, conveniently and comfortably fitted up with handsome mahogany counters, extending not only round the sides, but in the lower and upper rooms, forming a parallelogram in the middle. These counters, having at proper distance flaps or falling-doors, are in contiguity with each other, but are respectively distinguished by a small groove at a distance of every four feet of counter, the pannels of which are numbered with conspicuous figures.

The first room, which is entered from the square, is sixty-two feet long and thirty-six broad. The walls are hung with red cloth, and at the end are large mirrors, a conspicuous clock, fire-places, &c. The principal sale is jewellery, toys, books, prints, millinery &c. and is entirely conducted by females."

10. *The Zoological Gardens.* (page 48)

The pasture lands known as Marylebone Park Fields were the subject of a Commission early in the nineteenth century, and it was planned to build a palace there for the Prince Regent, connected with Carlton House by way of Regent Street. The laying-out of the Regent's Park began in 1812, and the park was opened to the public in 1838. Ten years earlier the Zoological Society had opened the gardens designed by Decimus Burton, and in 1839 the collection was augmented by the animals from the Tower and Windsor Castle. Visitors in Horne's day seem to have looked for the same kind of enjoyment from the Zoo as we do today.

11. *the Italian Opera.* (page 51)

Lady Flora was taken to the theatre on the corner of the Haymarket and Pall Mall, variously known as the King's and Her Majesty's Theatre, a theatre built between 1792 and 1820 on the site of an earlier one destroyed by fire. This theatre was the home of Italian Opera in England until Covent Garden was given the monopoly in 1847. The old Opera House was burned down in 1867.

12. . . . *as the poet Henry Chorley observes:*
"*When all that's feeble squeaks within the soul!*" (page 53)
A private joke, and a private revenge by Horne on Henry Chorley (1808–72), a critic who had been severe in the pages of the *Athenaeum* on the work of some of the unsuccessful dramatists who belonged to the Syncretic Society and were friends of Horne. In his remarks Chorley had often used the word "*feeble*". Horne explained the joke when he published a collection of letters to and from Elizabeth Barrett Browning in 1877. She had been amused to learn that Horne and Henry Chorley had met unexpectedly at Miss Mitford's and that the lady was unaware "what a meeting of thunderclouds it might be". Horne quotes the passage from the *London Doll* and continues:

"A copy of this little book had been sent by me to Mary Howitt. Mr Henry Chorley chanced to call upon her a morning or so afterwards, and Mary Howitt, with the innocence of a child of seven years old, placed the book in his hand, as she was leaving the room to attend to some domestic matter, calling his attention to the (assumed) quotation from 'the poet, Henry Chorley', as something complimentary that would please him." (S. R. Townshend Mayer: *Letters of E.B.B. to R.H.H.*, Vol. 1, 1877, pp. 237–8)

When Mary Howitt returned she found the poet in a state of discomposure—but, Horne says, "the scene is too ridiculous to pursue."

13. *to be taken to Willis's Rooms—in fact, she wanted to dance herself at "Almack's".* (page 63)

Almack's Assembly Rooms, in King Street, St James's, taken over by Willis in 1831, were ornately and lavishly decorated and provided accommodation for nearly a thousand. To the child of Horne's time the building would still be the ideal of glitter and fashion, but it was to be known not much later as the place where Thackeray and other literary lions gave lectures and readings.

14. *"the Exhibition of Pictures at the Royal Academy in Trafalgar Square . . . the Diorama in the Regent's Park . . . the Panorama in Leicester square . . . the British Museum".* (page 77)

The National Gallery was still very much in the public eye. When it was opened in 1838 it came under a fire of criticism for its mean conception, and was known as the National Cruet-Stand because of its pepper-pot cupolas. Only six rooms were devoted to the national collection, the rest being used by the Royal Academy of Arts until they moved to Burlington House.

The Diorama was probably one of the many exhibitions housed in the Colosseum, a vast circular building with glazed cupola and portico in the south-east corner of the park. The building was demolished in 1875 and is commemorated in the name of a block of houses in Albany Street.

A similar building in Leicester Square, the Panopticon, was designed after the Moorish style and dedicated to the cultivation of popular science. A Panorama would naturally find a place there. Not long after Horne wrote this story the Panopticon was sold by auction and the working models were dispersed; it later became a Theatre of Varieties.

The British Museum had been open since 1759 but until

1820 the public had to apply in advance for admission and only five parties of fifteen were admitted, on three days in the week.

By the choice of entertainment for Mary Hope, Horne has neatly placed her in her social sphere, midway between the milliner's apprentice and the Countess's daughter; she is a child whose education is taken seriously.

15. *"Clo'! clo'! clo'!"* (page 82)

The old Jew walking the street with his sack over his shoulder, with top hat, straggling beard and long frock coat, was a very familiar figure in the London of Horne and Mayhew—and for that matter, Dickens—and in Petticoat Lane the vast exchange for old clothes, entirely run by Jews, was just at this time being regulated by law. Mayhew estimated that there were some five or six hundred Jewish old clothes dealers in London in the 1840's, as against a thousand not much earlier, for a large immigration of Irish, working longer hours and less hampered by sectarian rules, were slowly ousting them from the streets.

16. *This boy had been used to carry a monkey about on the top of his organ.* (page 85)

Henry Mayhew records, in *London Labour and the London Poor*, that monkeys were forbidden in London at this time, but that there were some to be seen going round with organ-playing children, and some were taught to steal from bystanders.

17. *Gog and Magog.* (page 86)

These guardians of London City, dating from Henry V's reign or earlier, were once made of wicker and pasteboard, but carved wooden figures were substituted in 1708.

Nearly fifteen feet high, they stood on each side of the doors leading to the Council Chamber at the Guildhall. Gog held an old English weapon, a pole with a hanging chain and a globe studded with spikes, and Magog a shield and spear appropriate to his Roman costume. The wooden figures were burned with the roof of the Guildhall during the 1940 blitz.

18. . . . *off we went into the street, to the tune of 'I'd be a butterfly!' . . . So we walked slowly away, playing 'They're all nodding'*. (page 86–87)

Among the familiar tunes played by Marco are two, noted here, which are less well-known. 'I'd be a butterfly born in a bower' was one of the hundreds of songs written by Thomas Haynes Bayly; it was introduced at Drury Lane on 9 October, 1827, in *The Wealthy Widow*, a comedy by John Poole, and would seem to have been one of Bayly's most popular compositions. I have not been able to identify the line 'They're all nodding', which Marco has struck up obviously as a gibe at the pompous public dinner from which he and his sister have been turned away. It seems likely that Horne is really referring to the Scottish traditional song, 'We're a' noddin' '. Its popularity at this period can be judged from its inclusion in *Wilson's Edition of the Songs of Scotland* (1842); and Dickens writes of its "revived Caledonian melody" in Chapter XXXIX of *Bleak House* (1852).

19. *the Thames Tunnel.* (page 88)

Marc Isambard Brunel produced his first plans for the Thames Tunnel in 1820 and work began in 1825; but it was not until 1841 that he was able to walk through from one side of the river to the other. The tunnel, which ran from Wapping to Rotherhithe, was later sold to the East London railway, to form part of the line between Whitechapel and New Cross.

20. *Barclay and Perkins.* (page 98)
The brewery in Southwark, founded by Child and Halsey, was sold to Henry Thrale and on his death was disposed of on behalf of Johnson's Mrs Thrale, to David Barclay of the banking family. He put in his nephew, Robert Barclay, as partner, with Mr Thrale's manager, Perkins. Again Horne is placing his character, Lydia Thomson, in her social and geographical sphere by one or two careful details.

21. *the New Grand Christmas Pantomime . . . Drury-lane Theatre.* (page 104–5 et seq.)
This theatre was the fourth on this site, opened in 1812 and the work of Benjamin Wyatt. The pantomime which Maria Poppet describes in such detail, and which follows after a play in the fashion of the time, may well have been written by Horne. It is the traditional kind, with rhymed couplets and Harlequinade, which may still be seen at Christmas time in good repertory theatres in the provinces.

J. R. Planché, who himself introduced fairy extravaganzas, in the 1830's, as an alternative Christmas entertainment for the young, criticised the taste for expensive and pointless spectacles and transformation scenes on the stage. His blueprint for the "pretty story" which he preferred is much like Horne's, with the social disparity between the lovers, the "cross-grained old father" and the good fairy who changes the lovers into Harlequin and Columbine, "the old curmudgeon into Pantaloon and the body-servant into Clown". (*The Recollections and Reflections of J. R. Planché:* Tinsley Brothers 1872, vol. 2., pp. 137–8)

22. *the Tragedy of "Douglas".* (page 123)
This romantic tragedy by John Hume, first produced in
1756, was based on a Scottish ballad. With its sensational
story, it was still popular in Horne's day—and indeed, for
long afterwards; but presumably Horne, with his ambitions
for the English stage, was using the doll's voice here with a
satirical edge.

EDITIONS AND TEXT OF *MEMOIRS OF A LONDON DOLL*

Horne's story of the London doll was first published by Joseph Cundall, at 12, Old Bond Street, early in 1846 (it is listed in Bent's *Monthly Literary Advertiser* on May 11). The title page announced *Memoirs of a London Doll, Written by Herself. Edited by Mrs Fairstar*. An edition published by Henry G. Bohn, York Street, Covent Garden, in 1850 and 1855, is identical with the first edition except in having a smaller format and type. Both these editions have four illustrations by Margaret Gillies, entitled:

The London Doll and the Country Doll (frontispiece)
Ellen Plummy and Nanny Bell
Lady Flora's Dance
The Doll's Introduction to Mary Hope

(These four illustrations are reproduced in their original order in the endpapers of the present edition.) In the British Museum copy of the 1846 edition (catalogued under Fairstar) the illustrations are attractively hand-coloured. The copy would therefore have been priced at six shillings, as against four shillings without colour.

E. J. Shumaker in *A Concise Bibliography of the Complete Works of Richard H. Horne* (Granville, Ohio, 1943) gives an intermediate American edition with engravings by Baker from designs by Billings, published at Boston by Ticknor, Reed and Fields in 1852. I have not seen a copy of this edition nor of the edition published by Dean in 1862 and listed, in the *English Catalogue* (British Museum), as *Adventures of a London Doll*.

In 1893 Brentano's of New York published *Memoirs of a London Doll* and *The Doll and her Friends, or, Memoirs of the Lady Seraphina*, as dainty twin books, with green linen covers on which little girls dance over a silvered strip. Both stories are "edited by Mrs Fairstar". *The Doll and her Friends* was in fact the work of Julia Charlotte Maitland, who also wrote for children the lightly educative *Historical Charades* and a delightful animal story, *Cat and Dog or, Memoirs of Puss and the Captain*. Her doll story, probably first published in 1852, went into several editions. It may have been attributed to Horne partly because of the hint of a sequel about a Country Doll at the end of the story of the London Doll. Moreover, Margaret Gillies's first picture (in the hand-coloured edition) shows two little dolls, one obviously urban in a fashionably low-cut white dress and ringlets, the other wearing a brown stuff dress and a bonnet. Shumaker wrongly lists *The Doll and her Friends* as a posthumous work by Horne; his bibliography is incomplete and contains other errors.

Memoirs of a London Doll was rediscovered in the present century and published by Macmillan, New York, in 1922, with an introduction by Clara Whitehill Hunt and illustrations by Emma L. Brock. This was followed by Harrap's edition of 1923, which has a preface by Marion St John Webb and uses Emma Brock's pictures. In it Horne's long description of the Christmas pantomime (Chapter 16) was considerably cut. There has been no subsequent edition until the present one.

Brentano's edition of 1893 shows many small alterations from the earlier text and these were perpetuated in the twentieth century. I can find neither rhyme nor reason in these alterations. Sometimes they are simply printing errors. Once or twice phrases or whole lines are omitted, and there are a number of changes of words which could be either genuine errors or misunderstandings, or deliberate (and unnecessary) changes. For instance, Ellen Plummy is set to "sort small cakes" for Twelfth Night, and this is obviously what was intended; Brentano has "work small cakes". Again, when the little girls line the doll's dress "to make it set out, and not hang too loosely in the folds", the line in 1893 reads "to make it set off . . .", which makes no sense. Besides alterations in words, the 1893 edition has, as a whole, shorter paragraphs and an overplus of commas, mostly replacing Horne's freer dashes. I see no reason why readers should not now be perfectly comfortable with Horne's actual words and his careful publisher's actual production.

The text used here is that of the first edition, unaltered save for the correction of four literal errors. These are:

page 9 (of 1846 edition): *Marcett* instead of *Marcet*, the correct spelling, which Horne uses elsewhere.

page 32/33: an unnecessary repetition of the turn-over word, *Nanny*.

page 46 line 11: *Sprat* is misprinted *Spart*.

page 76 line 6: *she* is misprinted *he*.

The 1846 style of punctuation etc—sometimes idiosyncratic— is followed faithfully in the 1967 edition except for the correction of a few obviously unintentional mistakes or omissions. The 1967 type has been chosen to resemble that of 1846, and the title-page is in the style of the original.